Table of Contents

Unit 1: Vocabulary

Unit 2: Sentences

Unit 3: Grammar and Usage

Table of Contents continued

Table of Contents *continued*

Introduction

The National Council of Teachers of English and the International Reading Association prepared standards for the English language arts. These standards "grew out of current research and theory about how students learn—in particular, how they learn language." These standards address "what students should know and be able to do in the English language arts."

One standard is that students should be able to communicate effectively by learning the "language of wider communication," the forms of the English language that are most commonly identified as standard English. Students must recognize the importance of audience when they write and speak so they will be able to use the appropriate form of language for the intended audience. The standards acknowledge that "students need guidance and practice to develop their skills in academic writing. . . . They need to understand the varying demands of different kinds of writing tasks and to recognize how to adapt tone, style, and content for the particular task at hand." Again, students must "consider the needs of their audiences as they compose, edit, and revise."

Another standard emphasizes that "students apply knowledge of language structure, language conventions. . . ." Students need practice with accepted language conventions (e.g., capitalization, punctuation, grammar) in order to develop awareness and consistent application in their writing.

Language Practice is a program designed for students who require additional practice in the basics of effective writing and speaking. Focused practice in key grammar, usage, mechanics, and composition areas helps students gain ownership of essential skills. The logical sequence of the practice exercises, combined with a clear and concise format, allows for easy and independent use.

National Council of Teachers of English and International Reading Association, *Standards for the English Language Arts*, 1996.

Organization

Language Practice provides systematic, focused attention to just one carefully selected skill at a time. Rules are clearly stated at the beginning of each lesson. Key terms are introduced in bold type. The rules are then illustrated with examples and followed by meaningful practice exercises.

Lessons are organized around a series of units. They are arranged in a logical sequence beginning with vocabulary; progressing through sentences, grammar and usage, and mechanics; and culminating with composition skills.

Grades 3 through 8 include a final unit on study skills, which can be assigned as needed. This unit includes such skills as organizing information, following directions, using a dictionary, using the library, and choosing appropriate reference sources.

Skills are reviewed thoroughly in a two-page test at the conclusion of each unit. These unit tests are presented in a standardized test format. The content of each unit is repeated and expanded in subsequent levels as highlighted in the skills correlation chart on pages 6 and 7.

Use

Throughout the program, *Language Practice* stresses the application of language principles. In addition to matching, circling, or underlining elements in a predetermined sentence, lessons ask students to use what they have learned in an original sentence or in rewriting a sentence.

Language Practice is designed for independent use by students who have had instruction in the specific skills covered in these lessons. Copies of the activities can be given to individuals, pairs of students, or small groups for completion. They can also be used as a center activity. If students are familiar with the content, the worksheets can be homework for reviewing and reinforcing skills.

From the beginning, students feel comfortable with the format of the lessons. Each lesson is introduced with a rule at the top of the page and ends with a meaningful exercise at the bottom of the page. Each lesson is clearly labeled, and directions are clear and uncomplicated. Because the format is logical and consistent and the vocabulary is carefully controlled, most students can use *Language Practice* with a high degree of independence. As the teacher, this allows you the time needed to help students on a one-to-one basis.

Special Feature

The process approach to teaching writing provides success for most students. *Language Practice* provides direct support for the teaching of composition and significantly enhances those strategies and techniques commonly associated with the process-writing approach.

Each book includes a composition unit that provides substantial work with important composition skills, such as considering audience, writing topic sentences, selecting supporting details, taking notes, writing reports, and revising and proofreading. Also included in the composition unit is practice with various prewriting activities, such as clustering and brainstorming, which play an important role in process writing. The composition lessons are presented in the same rule-plus-practice format as in other units.

Additional Notes

- Parent Communication. Sign the *Letter to Parents* and send it home with the students. This letter offers suggestions for parental involvement to increase learner success.

- Assessment Test. Use the Assessment Test on pages 8 through 11 to determine the skills your students need to practice.

- Language Terms. Provide each student with a copy of the list of language terms on page 12 to keep for reference throughout the year. Also place a copy in the classroom language arts center for reference.

- Center Activities. Use the worksheets as center activities to give students the opportunity to work cooperatively.

- Have fun. The activities use a variety of strategies to maintain student interest. Watch your students' language improve as skills are applied in structured, relevant practice!

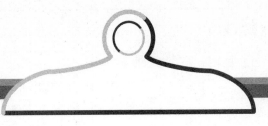

Dear Parent,

During this school year, our class will be working with a language program that covers the basics of effective writing and speaking. To increase your child's language skills, we will be completing activity sheets that provide practice to ensure mastery of these important skills.

From time to time, I may send home activity sheets. To best help your child, please consider the following suggestions:

- Provide a quiet place to work.
- Go over the rules, examples, and directions together.
- Encourage your child to do his or her best.
- Check the lesson when it is complete.
- Go over your child's work, and note improvements as well as concerns.

Help your child maintain a positive attitude about language skills. Let your child know that each lesson provides an opportunity to have fun and to learn. If your child expresses anxiety about these skills, help him or her understand what causes the stress. Then talk about ways to deal with it in a positive way.

Above all, enjoy this time you spend with your child. He or she will feel your support, and skills will improve with each activity completed.

Thank you for your help!

Cordially,

Skills Correlation

	1	2	3	4	5	6	7	8
Vocabulary								
Sound Words (Onomatopoeia)	■							
Rhyming Words	■	■						
Synonyms	■	■	■	■	■	■	■	■
Antonyms	■	■	■	■	■	■	■	■
Homonyms	■	■	■	■	■	■	■	■
Multiple Meanings/Homographs	■		■	■	■	■	■	■
Prefixes and Suffixes			■	■	■	■	■	■
Base and Root Words			■	■	■	■	■	■
Compound Words			■	■	■	■	■	■
Contractions			■	■	■	■	■	■
Idioms						■	■	■
Connotation/Denotation						■	■	■
Sentences								
Word Order in Sentences	■	■						
Recognizing a Sentence	■	■	■	■	■	■	■	■
Subjects and Predicates	■	■	■	■	■	■	■	■
Types of Sentences	■	■	■	■	■	■	■	■
Compound/Complex Sentences			■	■	■	■	■	■
Sentence Combining			■	■	■	■	■	■
Run-On Sentences					■	■	■	■
Independent and Subordinate Clauses							■	■
Compound Subjects and Predicates						■	■	■
Direct and Indirect Objects							■	■
Inverted Word Order						■	■	■
Grammar and Usage								
Common and Proper Nouns	■	■	■	■	■	■	■	■
Singular and Plural Nouns	■	■	■	■	■	■	■	■
Possessive Nouns			■	■	■	■	■	■
Appositives						■	■	■
Verbs	■	■	■	■	■	■	■	■
Verb Tense	■	■	■	■	■	■	■	■
Regular/Irregular Verbs	■	■	■	■	■	■	■	■
Subject/Verb Agreement		■	■	■	■	■	■	■
Verb Phrases						■	■	■
Transitive and Intransitive Verbs							■	■
Verbals: Gerunds, Participles, and Infinitives							■	■
Active and Passive Voice							■	■
Mood								■
Pronouns	■	■	■	■	■	■	■	■
Antecedents							■	■
Articles	■	■	■					
Adjectives	■	■	■	■	■	■	■	■
Correct Word Usage (e.g. *may/can, sit/set*)	■	■	■	■	■	■	■	■
Adverbs			■	■	■	■	■	■
Prepositions					■	■	■	■
Prepositional Phrases						■	■	■
Conjunctions						■	■	■
Interjections						■	■	■
Double Negatives								■
Capitalization and Punctuation								
Capitalization: First Word in Sentence	■	■	■	■	■	■	■	
Capitalization: Proper Nouns	■	■	■	■	■	■	■	■
Capitalization: in Letters		■	■	■	■	■	■	■

	1	2	3	4	5	6	7	8
Capitalization and Punctuation (cont'd)								
Capitalization: Abbreviations		■	■	■	■	■	■	■
Capitalization: Titles		■	■		■	■	■	■
Capitalization: Proper Adjectives					■	■	■	■
End Punctuation	■	■	■	■	■	■	■	■
Commas		■	■	■	■	■	■	■
Apostrophes in Contractions		■	■	■	■	■	■	■
Apostrophes in Possessives			■	■	■	■	■	■
Quotation Marks			■	■	■	■	■	■
Colons/Semicolons						■	■	■
Hyphens						■	■	■
Composition								
Expanding Sentences						■	■	■	■
Writing a Paragraph		■	■	■	■	■	■	■
Paragraphs: Topic Sentence (main idea)		■	■	■	■	■	■	■
Paragraphs: Supporting Details		■	■	■	■	■	■	■
Order In Paragraphs		■	■	■	■	■	■	■
Writing Process:								
Establishing Purpose			■	■		■	■	■
Audience					■	■	■	■
Topic			■	■	■	■	■	■
Outlining				■		■	■	■
Clustering/Brainstorming					■		■	■
Notetaking						■	■	
Revising/Proofreading					■	■	■	■
Types of Writing:								
Letter	■	■	■			■		
"How-to" Paragraph			■					
Invitation			■					
Telephone Message			■					
Conversation				■				
Narrative Paragraph				■				
Comparing and Contrasting					■			
Descriptive Paragraph					■			
Report						■		
Interview							■	
Persuasive Composition								■
Readiness/Study Skills								
Grouping	■							
Letters of Alphabet	■							
Listening	■	■						
Making Comparisons	■	■						
Organizing Information	■	■	■					
Following Directions	■	■	■	■	■			
Alphabetical Order	■	■	■	■	■	■	■	■
Using a Dictionary:								
Definitions		■	■	■	■	■	■	■
Guide Words/Entry Words		■	■	■	■	■	■	■
Syllables			■	■	■	■	■	■
Multiple Meanings						■	■	■
Word Origins						■	■	■
Parts of a Book						■	■	■
Using the Library						■	■	■
Using Encyclopedias				■	■	■	■	■
Using Reference Books						■	■	■
Using the *Readers' Guide*							■	■
Choosing Appropriate Sources						■	■	■

Name _____ Date _____

Assessment Test

A. Write S before each pair of synonyms, A before each pair of antonyms, and H before each pair of homonyms.

_____ **1.** good, bad   _____ **3.** big, large

_____ **2.** their, they're   _____ **4.** begin, start

B. Circle the correct definition for the underlined word in the sentence.

1. The snap made me look around.

sound made with fingers   a metal fastener

C. Write P before each word with a prefix, S before each word with a suffix, and C before each compound word.

_____ **1.** careless   _____ **3.** baseball

_____ **2.** misbehave   _____ **4.** reuse

D. Write a contraction for the underlined words.

_____ **1.** He will not go.   _____ **2.** I am tired.

E. Write D before the declarative sentence, IM before the imperative sentence, E before the exclamatory sentence, and IN before the interrogative sentence.

_____ **1.** That is a great shirt!   _____ **3.** I think it fits just fine.

_____ **2.** Can't you see that it's too big?   _____ **4.** Take it back to the store.

F. Draw a line between the subject and the predicate. Underline the simple subject once and the simple predicate twice.

1. It is raining outside.

2. There are puddles in the street.

G. Combine the sentences into one sentence.

Jerry went out to dinner. He went to the new restaurant.

_____

H. Separate the run-on sentence.

Alex cooked a big meal, he served it to his friends.

_____

Name _____ Date _____

I. Underline the common nouns, and circle the proper nouns in the sentence.

Betty chose two dogs, Yip and Yap, to take home to her children.

J. Write the correct possessive noun to complete the sentence.

The mailbox has a flag. The _____ flag is up.

K. Write A if the underlined verb is an action verb, L if it is a linking verb, or H if it is a helping verb.

_____ 1. Cyclone <u>ran</u> the race in record time.

_____ 2. After a rain the air <u>smells</u> clean.

_____ 3. We <u>are</u> walking daily for exercise.

L. Write past, present, or future to show the tense of each underlined verb.

_____ 1. They <u>will need</u> more ice soon.

_____ 2. Lee <u>told</u> his friend the truth.

_____ 3. She <u>saves</u> forty dollars a month.

M. Circle the correct verb in each sentence.

1. Soccer (is, are) a popular sport today.   2. Many fans will (come, came) to watch.

N. Complete each sentence by writing the correct pronoun for the words in parentheses.

1. Yesterday (Anika and I) _____ went to the library.

2. Then we met (our friends) _____ at the theater.

O. In the sentence below, underline each adjective, and circle each adverb.

We carefully planned an exciting surprise party for Henry.

P. Circle the correct word to complete each sentence.

1. No one (never, ever) comes to visit us.

2. (Them, Those) people (don't, doesn't) know what they're missing!

Name _____ Date _____

Q. In the letter below, underline letters that should be capitalized, and add punctuation where needed.

977 n seaside dr

ann arbor mi 68445

jan 25 19___

dear kathleen

    mario and i took ginger to the vet to get her shots ___ she really hates to go ___

    how is frisky ___ i hope you are both fine ___

                your friend

                elena

R. Rewrite the sentences below in paragraph form. Put the topic sentence first, and circle the time order words.

1. Then we spoke to the neighbors.
2. We just moved into a new house.
3. Finally, we had peace and quiet.
4. First, the dog next door began barking all night.

_____

_____

_____

_____

S. Using the words and phrases below, fill in the outline.

Name and number   Information needed from caller
Taking a phone message   Message

Statement: _____

    I. _____

        A. _____

        B. _____

T. Rewrite each list in alphabetical order. Then write the words that would be the guide words for each list.

Guide Words	Guide Words
_____ / _____	_____ / _____
1. right _____	1. bat _____
2. rock _____	2. back _____
3. rich _____	3. ball _____
4. rinse _____	4. base _____
5. rob _____	5. baby _____

U. Use the sample encyclopedia entry to answer the questions.

> **AUDUBON, JOHN JAMES** (1785–1851) was an artist. He came to North America in 1803 to study and draw birds. *See also* AUDUBON SOCIETY.

1. Who is the article about? _____

2. What is the cross-reference? _____

_____

V. Circle the word you would look under to find an article on each of the following. Then write the number of the volume in which you would find it.

A–C	D–F	G–I	J–L	M–N	O–Q	R–S	T–V	W–Z
1	2	3	4	5	6	7	8	9

_____ 1. the sea floor   _____ 7. the truth about vampires

_____ 2. Hong Kong   _____ 8. breeds of horses

_____ 3. nursing skills   _____ 9. the plays of Shakespeare

_____ 4. the life cycle of the fly   _____ 10. boomerangs as weapons

_____ 5. Helen Keller   _____ 11. string instruments

_____ 6. how aluminum is made   _____ 12. New Orleans

Language Terms

abbreviation a short form of a word

action verb a verb that tells an action that the subject is doing

adjective a word that describes a noun by telling <u>which one</u>, <u>what kind</u>, or <u>how many</u>

adverb a word that describes a verb

antonym a word that has the opposite meaning of another word

apostrophe a mark used to show where the missing letter or letters would be in a contraction

common noun a noun that does not name a particular person, place, or thing

compound sentence two simple sentences joined together by words such as <u>and</u>, <u>but</u>, <u>so</u>, and <u>or</u>

compound word a word formed by putting two or more words together

contraction a word formed by joining two other words

declarative sentence a sentence that makes a statement

exclamatory sentence a sentence that shows surprise or emotion

helping verb a word used to help the main verb of the sentence, usually a form of the verb <u>to be</u>

homonym a word that sounds like another word, but has a different meaning and is spelled differently

imperative sentence a sentence that gives a command

interrogative sentence a sentence that asks a question

linking verb a verb that does not show action, but links the subject to a word that either describes the subject or gives the subject another name

noun a word that names a person, place, or thing

object pronoun a pronoun used after an action verb or after words such as <u>to</u>, <u>with</u>, <u>for</u>, and <u>by</u>

paragraph a group of sentences about one main idea

plural noun a noun that names more than one person, place, or thing

possessive noun a noun that tells who or what owns something

possessive pronoun a pronoun that tells who or what owns something

predicate the part of a sentence that tells what the subject does or what happens to the subject

prefix a syllable added to the beginning of a word to change the meaning of the word

pronoun a word that takes the place of a noun

proper noun a noun that names a particular person, place, or thing and is capitalized

quotation tells the exact words a person said

run-on sentence two or more sentences that run together without correct punctuation

sentence a group of words that expresses a complete thought

simple predicate the main word or words in the predicate part of a sentence

simple sentence a sentence that has one subject and one predicate

simple subject the main word in the subject part of a sentence

singular noun a noun that names one person, place, or thing

subject the part of a sentence that tells who or what the sentence is about

suffix a syllable added to the end of a word to change the meaning of the word

synonym a word that has the same or almost the same meaning as another word

topic sentence a sentence that tells the main idea of a paragraph

verb the main word in the predicate

verb tense tells the time expressed by the verb

Synonyms

> ■ A **synonym** is a word that has the same or almost the same meaning as another word.
> EXAMPLES: last–final; leave–go; prize–award

A. For each underlined word, circle its synonym at the end of the sentence.

1. My goal is to become a biologist. (thought, desire)
2. I like going out into the field to study. (outdoors, lab)
3. The best learning comes through observing things in nature. (seeing, changing)
4. I record my findings in a journal. (write, tape)
5. Then I compare what I have seen to what books say. (question, match)
6. If there is a difference, I consult my teacher. (direct, ask)
7. Together we explore possible theories. (ideas, facts)
8. Sometimes there are only small differences between theories. (little, large)
9. I like studying plants the most. (enjoy, hate)
10. I raised some bean plants for an experiment. (grew, bought)
11. The experiment worked exactly as planned. (arranged, found)

B. Rewrite these sentences. Use synonyms from the box below for the underlined words.

active	brave	common	glad
halt	large	stay	uncommon

1. The ordinary hive has many worker bees.

   _____

2. It is not unusual to find 80,000 busy workers in a colony.

   _____

3. The fearless worker bee will do anything to stop the enemies of the hive.

   _____

4. The hive must remain warm, or the bees will die.

   _____

5. Farmers are happy to see big hives near their fields.

   _____

Antonyms

> ■ An **antonym** is a word that has the opposite meaning of another word.   EXAMPLES: stop—go; yes—no; hot—cold

A. For each underlined word, write an antonym from the box.

1. <u>dull</u> knife   _____ knife

2. <u>hard</u> cheese   _____ cheese

3. <u>correct</u> answer   _____ answer

4. <u>spend</u> money   _____ money

5. <u>remember</u> groceries   _____ groceries

6. <u>neat</u> room   _____ room

7. <u>finish</u> chores   _____ chores

8. <u>old</u> clothes   _____ clothes

9. <u>bottom</u> line   _____ line

begin
forget
messy
new
save
sharp
soft
top
wrong

B. Rewrite the paragraph using an antonym for each underlined word.

The <u>little</u> game was that evening. Scott and Jeff wanted to wear <u>dirty</u> uniforms. They believed that looking <u>bad</u> to the other team would help them win. They <u>dirtied</u> their uniforms at the same time. They used bleach to <u>fade</u> the colors. When they finished <u>washing</u> the uniforms, they discovered they had been <u>right</u>. Their uniforms were now the <u>opposite</u> color as those of the other team!

_____

_____

_____

_____

_____

_____

_____

_____

Homonyms

> ■ A **homonym** is a word that sounds like another word. However, it has a different meaning and is spelled differently.
> EXAMPLES: it's, its   their, there, and they're
> It's means "it is." **It's** a nice day.
> Its means "belonging to it." The dog hurt **its** leg.
> Their means "belonging to them." That is **their** house.
> There means "in or at that place." Put it **there**.
> They're means "they are." **They're** going to the game.

A. Write it's or its to complete each sentence.

1. The team starts _____ practice at noon.

2. The coach says _____ necessary to practice.

3. I don't believe the players think _____ fun to practice.

4. Others say _____ exciting to watch the game from the sidelines.

5. The team is proud of _____ record.

6. If the team does _____ job, it will win.

7. I think _____ still a month until the championship game.

8. The team thinks _____ chance for winning the championship

   is good.

9. However, _____ too early to know for sure.

B. Circle the correct homonym in each sentence.

1. (There, Their, They're) is no reason to believe something is wrong.
2. (There, Their, They're) only a few minutes late.
3. I'm sure (there, their, they're) fine and will be here soon.
4. You know (there, their, they're) habits.
5. Wherever they go, they get (there, their, they're) late.
6. (There, Their, They're) families are like that, too.
7. I don't understand why (there, their, they're) always late.
8. Maybe (there, their, they're) clocks are wrong!

More Homonyms

> ■ Remember that a **homonym** is a word that sounds like another
> word.   EXAMPLES: to, two, too   right, write   hear, here
> <u>To</u> means "toward" or "to do something." Go **to** the store.
> <u>Two</u> means "the number 2." Buy **two** gallons of milk.
> <u>Too</u> means "also" or "more than enough." It's **too** hot.
>
> <u>Write</u> means "to put words or numbers onto paper."
> Did you **write** the letter?
> <u>Right</u> means "correct" or "the opposite of left."
> Turn **right** at the corner.
>
> <u>Hear</u> means "listen." Didn't you **hear** me?
> <u>Here</u> means "in this place." Meet me **here** in one hour.

A. Write <u>to</u>, <u>two</u>, or <u>too</u> to complete each sentence.

1. It was _____ years ago that José and I went on
   vacation _____ the mountains.

2. We thought about going back last year, _____, but we
   decided not _____.

3. We both thought going _____ the beach would be more fun.

4. Since only _____ of us were going, we thought we'd meet more
   people there.

B. Write <u>right</u> or <u>write</u> to complete each sentence.

1. I'll _____ directions for finding my house.

2. You'll need a map to find the _____ roads.

3. Go ten miles and turn _____ at the bridge.

4. You're on the _____ road if you pass the mall.

C. Write <u>hear</u> or <u>here</u> to complete each sentence.

1. "I can't _____ you because of the music," shouted Alan.

2. "Come _____ so I can _____ you better," said Peter.

3. "Why did we come _____ to talk? I can't _____ anything,"
   said Alan.

4. "Let's get out of _____," said Peter.

Name _____   Date _____

Multiple Meanings

■ Some words have more than one meaning. They are spelled the same, and often are pronounced the same, but they mean different things. The only way to know the meaning of these words is to see how they are used in a sentence.
  EXAMPLES: I **can** go.   Get the **can** of beans.

A. Circle the correct meaning for each underlined word.

1. She put the pad behind her back and leaned against it.
   pillow   walk softly

2. A tear rolled down her cheek.
   rip or pull apart   salty liquid from the eye

3. The rain continued to beat against the little cabin.
   strike over and over   to mix

4. As she listened, the warning bell began to ring.
   make the sound of a bell   narrow circle of metal worn on the finger

5. The pounding waves made a terrible racket.
   light bat used in sports   loud noise

6. Her cabin would soon be lost to the storm.
   attack   heavy winds with rain or snow

7. Her only hope was that someone would come and lead her to safety.
   soft metal   guide

B. Write a sentence for each meaning of the words given.

1. wind: blowing air

   _____

   wind: to tighten the spring of

   _____

2. rock: to move back and forth

   _____

   rock: a large stone

   _____

Prefixes

> ■ A **prefix** is a syllable added to the beginning of a word to change the meaning of the word.
> EXAMPLES:
> The prefix <u>dis-</u> means "not" or "the opposite of." **dis**appear
> The prefix <u>mis-</u> means "bad(ly)" or "wrong(ly)." **mis**behave
> The prefix <u>re-</u> means "again" or "back." **re**do
> The prefix <u>un-</u> means "not" or "the opposite of." **un**friendly

A. Complete each sentence by adding <u>un-</u> or <u>dis-</u> to the word in parentheses.

1. Tabor the Great made a man _____ from the stage. (appear)

2. The man looked _____ about what would happen to him. (concerned)

3. He seemed _____ that he was even on the stage. (aware)

4. The man vanished! The audience tried to _____ where he'd gone. (cover)

5. But the man reappeared and was _____. (harmed)

6. It would be hard to _____ an act as great as Tabor's. (like)

7. No one could _____ with the fact that it had been a fine evening. (agree)

B. Complete each sentence by adding <u>mis-</u> or <u>re-</u> to the word in parentheses.

1. I _____ the plan for the park at the edge of town. (understood)

2. I didn't want to see a _____ of such fine land. (use)

3. The plan is to _____ our town as it was long ago. (create)

4. It will help us to _____ the history of the town. (live)

5. I really _____ the plan. (judged)

6. I should learn not to _____ before I know all the facts. (act)

Name _____ Date _____

Suffixes

> ■ A **suffix** is a syllable added to the end of a word to change the meaning of the word.
>
> EXAMPLES:
>
> The suffix -<u>ful</u> means "full of," "able to," or "the amount that will fill." hope**ful**, help**ful**, spoon**ful**
>
> The suffix -<u>less</u> means "without" or "not able to do." hope**less**, harm**less**

A. In each blank, write the word that matches the definition in parentheses.

effortless	worthless	meaningful	endless
successful	careless	joyless	tireless

1. Giving a _____ party is not always easy. (full of success)

2. When planning a party, I am _____. (not able to tire)

3. If the party is well planned, it looks _____. (without effort)

4. A _____ mistake can ruin a party. (without care)

5. A _____ game helps people to get into the spirit of the party.
   (full of meaning)

6. There is an _____ number of party games. (without end)

7. But all of the planning is _____ if no one comes.
   (without worth)

8. It would be a _____ evening if no one came to my party!
   (without joy)

B. Write a definition for the underlined word in each phrase.

1. <u>colorless</u> soap _____without color_____

2. <u>bottomless</u> pit _____

3. <u>sorrowful</u> event _____

4. <u>beautiful</u> car _____

5. <u>flavorless</u> meal _____

Unit 1, Vocabulary
© Steck-Vaughn Publishing Company

Language Practice 4, SV 7160-0

Compound Words

> ■ A **compound word** is a word formed by putting two or more words together.　EXAMPLES: railway, textbook

A. Write the two words that form each underlined compound word.

1. We are planning a picnic this <u>weekend</u>.

   _____   _____

2. Aunt Tess is bringing her delicious <u>homemade</u> chicken.

   _____   _____

3. My job is to bring the <u>watermelon</u>.

   _____   _____

4. The picnic will be over at <u>sunset</u>.

   _____   _____

**B. Combine words from the box to form compound words.
Use a compound word to complete each sentence.**

fire	front	watch	speaker	water	boat	place	tug	man	loud

1. The _____ inched slowly into the harbor.

2. The captain enjoyed looking at the buildings on the _____.

3. Using the _____, he called the crew to the deck.

4. As he waved to Mike, the night _____, he felt glad to be going home.

5. He would soon be home sitting in front of his warm _____.

C. Combine the words below to form four compound words. Use each word in a sentence of your own.

news	night	note	base	mid	ball	paper	book

1. _____   _____

2. _____   _____

3. _____   _____

4. _____   _____

Contractions

- A **contraction** is a word formed by joining two other words. When the two words are joined, a letter or letters are left out. An **apostrophe** (') is used to show where the missing letter or letters would be.

  EXAMPLE: I ~~would~~—I'd   he ~~is~~—he's   we ~~have~~—we've

- The only contraction that breaks this rule is won't. <u>Won't</u> means "will not." The <u>i</u> becomes <u>o</u> when the other letters are dropped.

A. Rewrite each sentence using a contraction for the words in parentheses.

1. (I will) need volunteers for the newspaper.

   _____

2. The first stories are due soon, so (we have) got to hurry.

   _____

3. (You will) each be given a section of the paper to work on.

   _____

4. Joyce says (she is) looking forward to the first copy.

   _____

5. Anthony says (he is) going to help us.

   _____

B. Underline the contraction in each sentence. Write the two words that make up each contraction.

1. Joe can't play in the basketball game tonight.

   _____   _____

2. He didn't remember to bring his uniform.

   _____   _____

3. The coach won't let him play without a uniform.

   _____   _____

4. Joe isn't happy about missing the game.

   _____   _____

5. No one thinks we'll win without Joe.

   _____   _____

Name _____   Date _____

Unit 1 Test

Choose the correct answer to each question.

Which word pairs are synonyms?

1. A ○ remain, see
   B ○ remain, stay
   C ○ remain, visit
   D ○ remain, avoid

2. A ○ throw, ball
   B ○ throw, pitch
   C ○ throw, run
   D ○ throw, threw

3. A ○ nation, country
   B ○ nation, world
   C ○ nation, city
   D ○ nation, state

4. A ○ simple, stupid
   B ○ simple, hard
   C ○ simple, wrong
   D ○ simple, easy

Which word pairs are antonyms?

5. A ○ cry, laugh
   B ○ cry, sing
   C ○ cry, hear
   D ○ cry, cough

6. A ○ smile, sing
   B ○ smile, lick
   C ○ smile, frown
   D ○ smile, weep

7. A ○ buy, by
   B ○ buy, sell
   C ○ buy, busy
   D ○ buy, greet

8. A ○ under, below
   B ○ under, stand
   C ○ under, cover
   D ○ under, over

Choose the homonym for each underlined word.

9. hear
   A ○ ear   C ○ here
   B ○ there   D ○ next

10. too
    A ○ also   C ○ one
    B ○ two   D ○ from

11. its
    A ○ his   C ○ hers
    B ○ it's   D ○ ours

12. their
    A ○ they're   C ○ our
    B ○ here   D ○ were

13. write
    A ○ wrong   C ○ left
    B ○ record   D ○ right

14. there
    A ○ here   C ○ their
    B ○ now   D ○ then

Name _____   Date _____

Choose the correct meaning for each underlined word.

15. He filled the <u>hole</u> with dirt.
    A ○ entire thing   **C** ○ empty space
    B ○ box   **D** ○ wagon

16. She wore a <u>plain</u> dress.
    A ○ striped   **C** ○ flat surface
    B ○ white   **D** ○ not fancy

17. The plants were in <u>rows</u>.
    A ○ straight lines   **C** ○ flowers
    B ○ moves with oars   **D** ○ roads

18. We <u>beat</u> the other team.
    A ○ a red vegetable   **C** ○ won against
    B ○ hit   **D** ○ lost

Choose the correct meaning for each underlined word.

19. <u>refill</u>
    A ○ not full
    B ○ fill
    C ○ empty
    D ○ fill again

20. <u>careful</u>
    A ○ reckless
    B ○ full of care
    C ○ care again
    D ○ without care

21. <u>unhappy</u>
    A ○ with joy
    B ○ glad
    C ○ not happy
    D ○ happy again

22. <u>careless</u>
    A ○ cautious
    B ○ without care
    C ○ safe
    D ○ mean

23. <u>misspell</u>
    A ○ spell wrong
    B ○ write
    C ○ spell again
    D ○ careless

24. <u>disagree</u>
    A ○ cross
    B ○ complain
    C ○ angry
    D ○ not agree

Choose the two words that can be combined to make a compound word.

25. A ○ under, over
    B ○ black, sea
    C ○ open, door
    D ○ air, plane

26. A ○ quick, fast
    B ○ shoe, lace
    C ○ did, not
    D ○ some, many

27. A ○ door, knob
    B ○ shoe, sock
    C ○ hat, coat
    D ○ them, they

Choose the two words that can be combined to make the underlined contraction.

28. Murray said <u>he'd</u> need more time.
    A ○ he will   **C** ○ he could
    B ○ he would   **D** ○ he did

29. He <u>isn't</u> finished with his project.
    A ○ are not   **C** ○ he is
    B ○ is not   **D** ○ I will

30. <u>They'd</u> go if they could.
    A ○ They have   **C** ○ They did
    B ○ They would   **D** ○ We would

31. <u>You'd</u> better be nice!
    A ○ You will   **C** ○ You are
    B ○ You were   **D** ○ You had

32. <u>We'll</u> wait until tomorrow.
    A ○ We would   **C** ○ We are
    B ○ We were   **D** ○ We will

33. It <u>shouldn't</u> be much longer.
    A ○ should let   **C** ○ should not
    B ○ should have   **D** ○ shall not

Recognizing a Sentence

> ■ A **sentence** is a group of words that expresses a complete thought.
>
>   EXAMPLES: Ralph washed the car. He drove to the store.

A. Write S on the line if the group of words is a sentence.

_____ **1.** Sarah ran to the car.

_____ **2.** She was in a big hurry.

_____ **3.** All of a sudden.

_____ **4.** Sarah stared at the car.

_____ **5.** She couldn't believe her eyes.

_____ **6.** Three of the tires.

_____ **7.** Were completely flat.

_____ **8.** Sarah had no idea what caused the flats.

_____ **9.** Up the driveway toward the house.

_____ **10.** An open box of nails.

B. Write S on the line if the group of words is a sentence. If it is not a sentence, rewrite it as a sentence by adding whatever is needed.

1. The parents' club has its monthly meeting tonight.

_____

2. All of the parents.

_____

3. A slide show about fire drills will be shown.

_____

4. Following the slide show.

_____

5. The parents will take information home.

_____

Name _____   Date _____

Declarative and Interrogative Sentences

> ■ A sentence that makes a statement is called a **declarative sentence.** EXAMPLE: We have two dogs.
> ■ A sentence that asks a question is called an **interrogative sentence.** EXAMPLE: Do you have a dog?

A. Write declarative if the sentence makes a statement. Write <u>interrogative</u> if the sentence asks a question.

_____ **1.** How are you today?

_____ **2.** You didn't look well yesterday.

_____ **3.** I hope you're not getting sick.

_____ **4.** Are you getting enough rest?

_____ **5.** You really can't afford to get sick.

_____ **6.** Isn't the big game this week?

_____ **7.** You need to be healthy for this game.

_____ **8.** Will you be here tomorrow?

_____ **9.** We are going to have a practice before the game.

_____ **10.** Are you ready for the game?

_____ **11.** Did you practice much?

_____ **12.** I practiced a lot.

_____ **13.** Do you think the practice will help?

_____ **14.** I get so nervous about big games.

_____ **15.** How do you stay so calm?

_____ **16.** Will you help me practice?

_____ **17.** I could use some help.

_____ **18.** You're really a good friend.

B. Write one declarative sentence and one interrogative sentence about sports.

1. _____

2. _____

Changing Sentences

- A statement can be made into a question by changing the order of the words in the sentence.   EXAMPLE: You are going to the show. Are you going to the show?
- Sometimes a question word like who, why, what, does, or how must also be added to the statement to change it to a question.   EXAMPLE: The show is two hours long. How long is the show?

A. Turn each statement into a question by changing the order of the words.

1. I am finished. _____

2. You shouldn't be finished. _____

3. This is taking too long. _____

4. You are leaving. _____

5. You can stay. _____

B. Turn the statements below into questions. You may change the order of the words and add question words as needed.

1. Joe starts his new job today.

   _____

2. He begins at nine o'clock.

   _____

3. He will leave home at eight o'clock.

   _____

4. Joe likes to work on cars.

   _____

5. Repairing cars is very interesting.

   _____

6. Joe is sure he will like this job.

   _____

7. Joe will do a good job.

   _____

Name _____   Date _____

Imperative and Exclamatory Sentences

> ■ A sentence that gives a command is called an **imperative sentence.**
>   EXAMPLES: Sit down. Read your book.
> ■ A sentence that shows surprise or emotion is called an **exclamatory sentence.**
>   EXAMPLES: Oh, you scared me! We won the game!

A. Write imperative if the sentence gives a command. Write exclamatory if the sentence shows surprise or emotion.

_____ **1.** You go first, Jack.

_____ **2.** Tell me if it's safe.

_____ **3.** I'm scared!

_____ **4.** Keep your voice down.

_____ **5.** I can't see!

_____ **6.** I'm lost!

_____ **7.** Be quiet.

_____ **8.** Come down here, Pete.

_____ **9.** I'm falling!

_____ **10.** Hurray, I'm out!

_____ **11.** Close the window.

_____ **12.** Watch out for that car.

B. Pretend that you are walking with a friend in a deep, dark forest. Write three imperative sentences and three exclamatory sentences.

1. _____

2. _____

3. _____

4. _____

5. _____

6. _____

Name _____ Date _____

Subjects and Predicates

> ■ Every sentence has two parts. The **subject** of a sentence tells who or what the sentence is about. The **predicate** tells what the subject does or what happens to the subject.
> EXAMPLE: <u>The marching band</u> <u>won the state championship.</u>
> **Subject**—The marching band; **Predicate**—won the state championship

A. Add a subject to each predicate to make a sentence.

1. _____ play tennis.   3. _____ returned the ball.

2. _____ run.   4. _____ won the game.

B. Add a predicate to each subject to make a sentence.

1. Players _____ .   3. Coaches _____ .

2. Some fans _____ .   4. Judges _____ .

C. Write <u>subject</u> or <u>predicate</u> to tell which part of each sentence is underlined.

_____ 1. <u>Tennis</u> is a game.

_____ 2. It <u>is played with a racket.</u>

_____ 3. The player <u>swings the racket.</u>

_____ 4. <u>A ball</u> is also needed.

_____ 5. Two or four players <u>may play at one time.</u>

_____ 6. <u>Love</u> means zero points in tennis.

_____ 7. A set <u>is won in six games.</u>

D. Draw one line under each subject and two lines under each predicate.
1. Tennis was invented by Major Walter Wingfield.
2. The game was called tennis-on-the-lawn.
3. Mary Outerbridge brought the game to the United States.
4. Tennis is a popular game.
5. Steffi Graf is a famous tennis player.
6. You can play tennis, too.

Simple Subjects and Predicates

- The **simple subject** is the main word in the subject part of a sentence. The simple subject is usually a noun or a pronoun.
- The **simple predicate** is the main word or words in the predicate. The simple predicate is a verb and any helping verbs it may have.

    EXAMPLE: My cousin keeps his car in the garage.

    Simple Subject — cousin
    Simple Predicate — keeps

A. Underline each subject. Then circle each simple subject within each subject.

1. The plans for a new car are made years ahead of time.
2. Many important decisions go into the design of a car.
3. Each part of the car is studied.
4. A clay model is made to show what the car will look like.

B. Underline each predicate. Then circle the simple predicate within each predicate.

1. Seven kinds of bears live in the world.
2. Most bears live in areas north of the equator.
3. Bears have small eyes.
4. Bears can live as long as thirty years.
5. A bear uses its claws to dig for food.
6. Brown bears usually eat grasses, berries, and nuts.
7. Seals and other animals are food for a polar bear.
8. Most bears sleep all winter.
9. Pandas are not really bears at all.

C. Write the simple subject and the simple predicate of each sentence.

1. The first basketball game was played in 1891.

    _____   _____

2. College teams played the sport in 1896.

    _____   _____

3. The first Olympic basketball game was in 1936.

    _____   _____

Simple and Compound Sentences

> ■ A **simple sentence** has one subject and one predicate.
>   EXAMPLE: <u>Fresh paint</u> <u>brightens a room</u>.
> ■ A **compound sentence** is two simple sentences joined together by words such as <u>and</u>, <u>but</u>, <u>so</u>, and <u>or</u>.
>   EXAMPLE: <u>I</u> <u>painted the den</u>, **and** <u>Kim</u> <u>painted the kitchen</u>.

A. Write <u>simple</u> or <u>compound</u> before each sentence.

_____ 1. We wanted to go camping, so we had to make plans.

_____ 2. I voted for Yosemite, but Sam voted for the Grand Canyon.

_____ 3. Sam got his way.

_____ 4. Finally, the day to start arrived.

_____ 5. I drove the camper, and Sam followed in the car.

_____ 6. The scenery was wonderful.

_____ 7. The canyon is almost too big to look real.

_____ 8. We wanted to camp at the rim, but it was too crowded.

_____ 9. We could sleep in the open, or we could use a tent.

_____ 10. We decided to use a tent.

B. Make a compound sentence by adding a simple sentence to each group of words below.

1. Sleeping outside is fun, but

_____

2. The Grand Canyon is a great place to visit, and

_____

3. We could hike down the canyon, or

_____

4. Canyon burros look friendly, but

_____

Name _____ Date _____

Combining Sentences

> ■ Short sentences about the same subject can often be **combined** into one sentence. Connecting words such as and, but, and or may be used to combine sentences.
>   EXAMPLE: Sam went to the store. Joan went to the store, too. They went in a red car. **Combined sentence**—Sam and Joan went to the store in a red car.

A. Combine each pair of sentences.

1. We have to write a report. The report is on history.

   _____

2. My subject is the Civil War. My subject is Robert E. Lee.

   _____

3. We must use the encyclopedia. We must use other books.

   _____

4. I should stop wasting time. I should start my report.

   _____

B. Combine each set of sentences into one sentence.

1. Juan bought a horse. It is big. The horse is brown.

   _____

2. The horse is kept in a barn. The barn is red. The barn is old.

   _____

3. Juan rides the horse. Lynn rides the horse. They ride in a field.

   _____

C. Write three short sentences about an animal. Then combine your sentences into one sentence.

   _____

   _____

   _____

   _____

Avoiding Run-on Sentences

- A **run-on sentence** is two or more sentences that run together without correct punctuation. Correct a run-on sentence by making separate sentences from its parts.
  EXAMPLE: Many plants have seeds, the seeds grow into more plants, then those plants have seeds. **Correction**—Many plants have seeds. The seeds grow into more plants. Then those plants have seeds.

- **Rewrite each story by separating each run-on sentence.**

One morning we found a baby bird it had been knocked from its nest by high winds its mother was nowhere to be seen. It was too young to fly, we took it inside to care for it. We were excited about taking care of the bird, we didn't know what to do about feeding it.

1. _____

2. _____

3. _____

4. _____

5. _____

6. _____

7. _____

The bird's little mouth flew open so often that we could not find enough insects to feed it. Then we found that the little bird liked dog food it also liked little bits of cooked egg yolk we even made some worms out of hamburger meat.

1. _____

2. _____

3. _____

4. _____

Name _____ Date _____

Unit 2 Test

Choose the group of words that is a sentence.

1. **A** ○ Wanted more time.
   B ○ Said our story.
   C ○ That he couldn't wait.
   D ○ He saved for a new car.

2. **A** ○ She almost.
   B ○ Diane worked hard.
   C ○ Late every day.
   D ○ She was very.

3. **A** ○ The horse grazed.
   B ○ On green grass.
   C ○ Ate a great deal.
   D ○ Ran around.

4. **A** ○ Asked a question.
   B ○ The answer.
   C ○ Told the truth.
   D ○ You were right.

Choose whether each sentence is declarative, interrogative, imperative, or exclamatory.

5. Did you study for the test?
   A ○ declarative
   B ○ interrogative
   C ○ imperative
   D ○ exclamatory

6. Oh, no, I forgot the test!
   A ○ declarative
   B ○ interrogative
   C ○ imperative
   D ○ exclamatory

7. Answer these questions.
   A ○ declarative
   B ○ interrogative
   C ○ imperative
   D ○ exclamatory

8. I don't know if I can.
   A ○ declarative
   B ○ interrogative
   C ○ imperative
   D ○ exclamatory

Choose the sentence that changes the underlined sentence to the type of sentence in parentheses.

9. Hand me that bowl. (interrogative)
   A ○ Give me that bowl.
   B ○ Hand me that bowl!
   C ○ Will you hand me that bowl?
   D ○ You handed me that bowl.

10. Did you pick up the mail? (declarative)
    A ○ You picked up the mail.
    B ○ Pick up the mail.
    C ○ Will you pick up the mail?
    D ○ Hurry and pick up the mail!

11. Would you like to go to a movie? (imperative)
    A ○ You would like to go to a movie.
    B ○ Are you going to a movie?
    C ○ Go to a movie.
    D ○ Let's go to a movie!

12. I think I'm lost. (exclamatory)
    A ○ Am I lost?
    B ○ I am lost.
    C ○ Don't tell me I'm lost.
    D ○ I'm lost!

Choose the correct answer to each question.

13. Which sentence has the subject underlined?

    A ○ <u>Jerry needed</u> a research project.

    B ○ He didn't <u>have an idea.</u>

    C ○ He thought <u>about electricity.</u>

    D ○ <u>Cindi</u> gave him some ideas.

14. Which sentence has the simple subject underlined?

    A ○ <u>He</u> couldn't decide.

    B ○ <u>He</u> needed more time.

    C ○ Jerry went to <u>Cindi.</u>

    D ○ <u>She</u> said she would help.

15. Which sentence has the simple subject and the simple predicate underlined?

    A ○ The <u>cat</u> <u>jumped</u> on the bed.

    B ○ <u>It</u> <u>was running</u> from the dog.

    C ○ The <u>dog</u> <u>chased</u> it.

    D ○ The <u>cat</u> <u>was</u> finally <u>safe.</u>

16. Which sentence has the simple predicate underlined?

    A ○ Cindi <u>asked</u> him what he liked.

    B ○ She <u>asked him questions.</u>

    C ○ They <u>chose</u> three subjects.

    D ○ Jerry <u>had to pick one of them.</u>

17. Which sentence has the predicate underlined?

    A ○ He <u>still couldn't</u> decide.

    B ○ Jerry <u>went to the library.</u>

    C ○ He <u>saw many books</u> on engines.

    D ○ Jerry <u>finally</u> picked engines.

18. Which sentence has the subject and the predicate underlined?

    A ○ <u>Mary</u> <u>found a wooden</u> chest.

    B ○ Her <u>sister</u> <u>helped her open it.</u>

    C ○ <u>They</u> <u>found an old diary</u> in there.

    D ○ <u>They</u> <u>read it with interest.</u>

Choose the sentence that is a simple sentence.

19. A ○ We can run, or we can walk.

    B ○ Let's walk together.

    C ○ You are fast, and I am slow.

    D ○ He will run, so I'll follow.

Choose the sentence that is a compound sentence.

20. A ○ I'll do it that way.

    B ○ You can watch me.

    C ○ I'll start it, and you can finish it.

    D ○ It's not the same.

Choose the sentence that correctly combines each set of sentences.

21. We bought a house. It is white. It is big.

    A ○ The big white house is ours.

    B ○ We bought a big white house.

    C ○ We bought a new house.

    D ○ Is our house big and white?

22. She sold her book. It is a novel. It is new.

    A ○ Her novel is new.

    B ○ Her new book is a novel.

    C ○ She sold her new novel.

    D ○ Did she sell her new novel?

Name _____   Date _____

Nouns

> ■ A **noun** is a word that names a person, place, or thing.
>   EXAMPLES: person–woman, Anna; place–city, San Francisco;
>   thing–dog, Fido

A. Underline the two nouns in each sentence.

1. Mrs. Smith has a big job ahead.
2. She needs to plan a picnic for her family.
3. Mrs. Smith must find a big park.
4. The family always enjoys the picnic.
5. It is a big event every year.
6. Mr. Smith is planning some games.
7. He will set up a net for volleyball.
8. Margie will make the hamburgers.
9. Mrs. Smith finally picked Riverview Park.
10. The park is on the Mississippi River.

B. Tell what each underlined noun is by writing person, place, or thing.

_____   1. Buttons the dog

_____   2. my brother John

_____   3. the neighbor's uncle

_____   4. 472 Elm Street

_____   5. Orville's friend

_____   6. Morris the cat

_____   7. the city of Trenton

_____   8. presented by the mayor

_____   9. Sydney, Australia

_____   10. my friend's sister

_____   11. the state of Utah

_____   12. a large cloud

_____   13. a happy clown

Name _____   Date _____

Proper and Common Nouns

- A **proper noun** names a particular person, place, or thing. It begins with a capital letter.
    EXAMPLES: person—Mary; place—Dayton; thing—Queenie
- A **common noun** does not name a particular person, place, or thing.
    EXAMPLES: person—girl; place—city; thing—house

A. Underline the common nouns in each sentence.

1. My cousin Monica will visit for the holidays.
2. She loves Thanksgiving in the country.
3. My cousin is always a welcome visitor.
4. Her stories about New York are interesting.
5. This year, she is bringing Dr. Alvarado with her.

B. Underline the proper nouns in each sentence.

1. Dr. Alvarado is a doctor in New York.
2. She works at Parkside Hospital.
3. In September, she's going to teach a class in medicine.
4. The class will be at Roosevelt University in Queens, New York.
5. The students come from all over the United States.

C. Write a proper noun for each common noun given.

1. dog _____Spot_____
2. country _____
3. name _____
4. day _____
5. city _____
6. holiday _____
7. month _____
8. uncle _____
9. cat _____
10. friend _____
11. state _____
12. father _____
13. game _____
14. street _____
15. planet _____
16. school _____
17. teacher _____
18. continent _____
19. president _____
20. magazine _____

Name _____   Date _____

Singular and Plural Nouns

> - A **singular noun** names one person, place, or thing.
> - A **plural noun** names more than one person, place, or thing.
> - Add -s to most nouns to make them plural.
>   EXAMPLE: dog—dogs
> - Add -es to nouns ending in s, z, x, ch, or sh to make them plural.
>   EXAMPLES: dress—dresses, box—boxes
> - If a noun ends in a vowel and y, add -s to make it plural. If the noun ends in a consonant and y, change the y to i and add -es.
>   EXAMPLES: bay—bays, party—parties
> - If a noun ends with the f sound, change the f to v and add -es.
>   EXAMPLE: calf—calves
> - Sometimes the entire spelling is changed to form a plural noun.
>   EXAMPLES: child—children, goose—geese, mouse—mice

A. Write S before each singular noun below. Then write its plural form. Write P before each plural noun. Then write its singular form. You may wish to check the spellings in a dictionary.

_____ 1. porch _____   _____ 8. halves _____

_____ 2. chair _____   _____ 9. pencil _____

_____ 3. girls _____   _____ 10. alley _____

_____ 4. wife _____   _____ 11. leaves _____

_____ 5. flies _____   _____ 12. pouch _____

_____ 6. sky _____   _____ 13. inches _____

_____ 7. foxes _____   _____ 14. shelf _____

B. Circle the correct noun in parentheses. Write singular or plural on the lines.

_____ 1. After dinner we watch two (program, programs).

_____ 2. We limit our television viewing to one (hour, hours) a day.

_____ 3. The rest of the (time, times), we read or just chat about our day.

_____ 4. Our (family, families) has grown closer since we started this habit.

_____ 5. In fact, Lupe now prefers one of her (magazines, magazine) to TV.

_____ 6. I still like to watch a good (show, shows) now and then.

Singular Possessive Nouns

> - A **possessive noun** is a noun that tells who or what owns something.
> - Add an **apostrophe** (') and an -s to the end of most singular nouns to show that they are possessive nouns.
>   EXAMPLES: Tony's house, the dog's bone

A. Rewrite each of the phrases below using a possessive noun.

1. the house of my aunt   _____ my aunt's house _____

2. the dog my cousin has   _____

3. the books belonging to my friend _____

4. the bicycle of my brother   _____

5. an apron belonging to the cook _____

B. Write the correct possessive form of the word in parentheses to complete each sentence.

1. (Jerry) _____ car was stolen.

2. The police (officer) _____ response was not encouraging.

3. He said the (thief) _____ trail was already cold.

4. He reported the (automobile) _____ last location.

5. Jerry hopes his (city) _____ police department will find it.

C. Write the correct possessive noun to complete the second sentence in each pair of sentences.

1. The store is having a sale. The _____ sale will last a week.

2. Lisa bought a coat. _____ coat has a heavy lining.

3. A clerk helped Lisa. The _____ job was to help people.

4. One shopping bag broke. The _____ contents spilled.

5. Another man helped her. Lisa was grateful for the

   _____ kindness.

Name _____   Date _____

Plural Possessive Nouns

- A **plural possessive** noun shows ownership by more than one person or thing.
- If a plural noun does not end in -s, the possessive is formed by adding an apostrophe and an -s ('s) to the noun.
  EXAMPLE: men's teams
- If a plural noun ends in -s, the possessive is usually formed by simply adding an apostrophe after the -s (s').
  EXAMPLE: birds' nests

A. Write the correct plural possessive form of the word in parentheses to complete each sentence.

1. My (sisters) _____ band is very popular.

2. The (uniforms) _____ colors are beautiful.

3. The band plays for (parents) _____ clubs.

4. The (members) _____ cheering was loud.

5. The (instruments) _____ sounds were perfect.

B. Write the correct possessive noun to complete the second sentence in each pair of sentences.

1. Fred and Carol are farmers. _____ Farmers' _____ work can be very hard.

2. Their children help on the farm. Fred depends on the

   _____ help.

3. There are three ponds on the farm. The _____ water is very clear.

4. Fred keeps many sheep on his farm. He prepares the

   _____ food.

5. He gets milk from his cows. The _____ milking time is very early.

6. Three huge barns hold the animals. Painting the _____ walls is a hard job.

Action Verbs

> ■ The **verb** is the main word in the predicate. If the verb tells an action that the subject is doing, it is called an **action verb.**
> EXAMPLES: Children **play** in the park. The squirrel **ran** up the tree.

A. Underline the action verb in each sentence.

1. Rex jumped at Tiger.
2. Tiger leaped for the tree.
3. Rex snapped back at the end of his rope.
4. Tiger quickly spun around.
5. Tiger arched her back.
6. Rex pulled against his rope.
7. Tiger danced sideways.
8. Rex howled loudly.
9. Then Tiger licked a furry paw.
10. She yawned slowly.
11. Rex chewed at the old rope.
12. He snarled at the cat.
13. Tiger teased Rex even more.
14. Rex pulled against the rope again.
15. Suddenly, it snapped.
16. Tiger shot into the air.
17. Rex bounded across the yard.
18. Tiger scrambled up the tree just in time.

B. Complete each sentence by adding a predicate with an action verb to each subject.

1. The captain of the team _____.
2. The coach _____.
3. All of the team members _____.
4. The fans _____.
5. The scorekeeper _____.
6. Everyone _____.

Linking Verbs

> ■ A **linking verb** does not show action. Instead, it links the subject to a word that either describes the subject or gives the subject another name. If a verb can be replaced by one of the verbs of being (<u>am</u>, <u>is</u>, <u>are</u>, <u>was</u>, <u>were</u>), then it is a linking verb.
>   EXAMPLES: Football **is** exciting. (<u>Exciting</u> describes football.)
>   They **were** a tired group. (<u>Group</u> is another name for <u>They</u>.)
>   Yoko **grew** tired. (<u>Grew</u> can be replaced by <u>is</u> without changing the sentence.)

A. Complete each sentence with a different linking verb from the box.

are	feel	is	seem	sound
become	grow	look	smells	taste

1. Spring _____ a wonderful time of year.

2. The days _____ warm.

3. The air _____ fresh.

4. The flowers _____ pretty.

5. The evenings _____ lighter.

6. Spring vegetables _____ fresh.

7. The birds _____ cheerful.

8. We _____ more active.

B. Write <u>L</u> in front of each sentence that has a linking verb.

_____ 1. The day seemed dreary.

_____ 2. We decided to stay inside.

_____ 3. It was too cold and rainy outdoors.

_____ 4. Jenny started a roaring fire.

_____ 5. We were warm and cozy.

_____ 6. We felt comfortable.

Helping Verbs

> ■ A **helping verb** is sometimes used to help the main verb of a sentence. Helping verbs are often forms of the verb to be— <u>am</u>, <u>is</u>, <u>are</u>, <u>was</u>, <u>were</u>. The verbs <u>has</u>, <u>have</u>, and <u>had</u> are also used as helping verbs.   EXAMPLES: Jerry **has** gone to the store. I **am** watching for the bus.

■ **Circle the helping verb and underline the main verb in each sentence.**

1. For a long time, we had wanted to give Sherry a surprise party.

2. We had planned the party in the park the day before her birthday.

3. She has gone to the park almost every day.

4. We were waiting for her there.

5. Sherry was raking her yard.

6. We were looking around the park for her.

7. We couldn't find her.

8. We were forced to make other plans.

9. So Sherry was given her surprise party on her birthday.

10. Juana is going to the zoo today.

11. She has gone there once before.

12. Jack had told her to see the monkeys.

13. She was going last week.

14. She had planned a picnic.

15. I am going to the zoo with her.

16. I have seen the zoo before.

17. We are taking the bus.

18. Jack is meeting us there.

19. He is riding his bike.

20. We are looking forward to our zoo visit.

Verb Tenses

■ The **tense** of a verb tells the time expressed by the verb.
  There are three tenses—present, past, and future.
■ **Present tense** tells about what is happening now.
  EXAMPLE: I **am walking** my dog. I **walk** my dog.
■ **Past tense** tells about something that happened before.
  EXAMPLE: I **walked** my dog yesterday.
■ **Future tense** tells about something that will happen.
  EXAMPLE: I **will walk** my dog tonight.

A. Write present, past, or future to tell the tense of each underlined verb.

_____ 1. Jules Verne <u>wrote</u> about going to the moon.

_____ 2. Spaceships <u>were</u> still in the future.

_____ 3. Now we <u>can fly</u> to the moon.

_____ 4. A space shuttle <u>will lift</u> off tomorrow.

_____ 5. It <u>is stationed</u> in Florida.

_____ 6. The shuttle <u>helped</u> us explore space.

_____ 7. It <u>will help</u> us settle in space.

_____ 8. The shuttle <u>is taking</u> off now.

_____ 9. It <u>will return</u> in a week.

_____ 10. I <u>will go</u> to watch it land.

_____ 11. It <u>will be</u> a sight to remember.

B. Complete each sentence by writing a verb in the tense shown in parentheses.

(past)   1. Joy _____ in the garden.

(present) 2. She _____ gardening.

(future)   3. The garden _____ many vegetables.

(present) 4. Joy _____ the garden to be nice.

(future)   5. She _____ flowers next week.

(past)   6. She _____ the garden last week.

Regular Verbs

- The past tense of a **regular verb** is usually formed by adding -ed.
    EXAMPLE: jump—jumped
- If the word ends with a single consonant that has one vowel before it, double the final consonant and add -ed.
    EXAMPLE: skip—skipped
- If the word ends with a silent e, drop the e and add -ed.
    EXAMPLE: bake—baked
- If the root word ends in y, change the y to i and add -ed.
    EXAMPLE: worry—worried

A. Write the past tense of each verb to complete each sentence.

1. Ms. Willis (look) _____ out the window.

2. She (gasp) _____ at what she saw.

3. A hot-air balloon (settle) _____ onto her lawn.

4. Two men (step) _____ from the balloon.

5. Ms. Willis (hurry) _____ across the yard.

6. The balloon's basket (crush) _____ her flower bed.

7. One man (scratch) _____ his head in wonder.

8. He said they were (head) _____ for the fairgrounds.

9. The wind had (change) _____.

10. "We (drop) _____ in here instead," he said.

B. Rewrite each phrase in the past tense.

1. sail the boat

_____

2. steer a straight course

_____

3. carry the sail

_____

4. enjoy the fresh air and sunshine

_____

Irregular Verbs

> ■ Do not add **-ed** to form the past tense of **irregular verbs.**
> Change the spelling in a different way.   EXAMPLES:
>
> | Present | Past | Present | Past | Present | Past |
> |---------|------|---------|------|---------|------|
> | begin | began | give | gave | say | said |
> | break | broke | go | went | see | saw |
> | choose | chose | grow | grew | sit | sat |
> | come | came | know | knew | take | took |
> | fall | fell | leave | left | throw | threw |
> | fly | flew | run | ran | write | wrote |

■ **Complete each sentence by writing the past tense of the verb in parentheses.**

1. Monday I (go) _____ to a singing tryout.

2. I got up and (leave) _____ early.

3. I (take) _____ the address but couldn't find the building.

4. Finally, I (know) _____ I needed to ask for directions.

5. I (grow) _____ worried that I would miss my turn.

6. Then I (see) _____ a sign on a building.

7. It (give) _____ a list of the companies in the building.

8. I (sit) _____ on a bench for a few minutes to calm down.

9. I (come) _____ to the right place after all.

10. Then I (fly) _____ upstairs to the office.

11. A man at the front desk frowned and (say) _____ I was late.

12. He (begin) _____ by handing me a form.

13. I (write) _____ my name, address, and phone number.

14. Then the pencil lead (break) _____.

15. He took it from me and (throw) _____ it away.

16. I (choose) _____ another one from his desk.

17. On the way back to my chair, I slipped and (fall) _____

18. The man (run) _____ to help me.

Name _____ Date _____

Making Subjects and Verbs Agree

> - The **subject** and **verb** of a sentence must agree in number.
> - A **singular** subject must have a singular verb.
> - A **plural** subject must have a plural verb.
> - <u>You</u> and <u>I</u> must have a plural verb.
>   EXAMPLES: Mike **hits.** They **hit.** I **hit.** You **hit.**
> - The singular form of a verb usually ends in -s or -es. Add -es to verbs that end in -s, -x, -z, -sh, and -ch.
>   EXAMPLES: Juan **watches** the game. Amy **waxes** the car.

- Circle the verb that agrees with the subject of each sentence.
  Write <u>singular</u> or <u>plural</u> to show the number of the subject and verb.

1. Chickens (eat, eats) grain. _____plural_____

2. A chicken (lives, live) on the ground. _____

3. They (flies, fly) very little. _____

4. A farmer (feeds, feed) the chickens every day. _____

5. Chickens (scratches, scratch) the ground for food. _____

6. Forest fires (causes, cause) damage every year. _____

7. A forest fire (destroys, destroy) large areas. _____

8. People (fights, fight) a fire with water and chemicals. _____

9. A firebreak (slows, slow) down a fire. _____

10. A river (acts, act) as a firebreak. _____

11. Airplanes (drops, drop) water on forest fires. _____

12. A firefighter always (watches, watch) for danger. _____

13. High winds (spreads, spread) forest fires. _____

14. A forest fire (kills, kill) many trees. _____

15. Many animals (loses, lose) their homes. _____

16. A forest (need, needs) many seasons to recover. _____

17. Responsible people (helps, help) prevent forest fires. _____

Making Subjects and Linking Verbs Agree

- A **linking verb** is either singular or plural. The linking verb must match the subject of the sentence in number.
  EXAMPLES: Singular—The movie **is** shown twice daily.
  Plural—Both movies **are** shown twice daily.
- A linking verb can be in the present tense or past tense.
  EXAMPLES: Present tense—The movie **is** shown twice daily.
  Past tense—Both movies **were** shown twice daily.
- Use there is or there was with one person, place, or thing.
- Use there are or there were with more than one.
  EXAMPLES: There **is** a movie tonight. There **are** many movies showing at that theater.

A. Write am, is, are, was, or were to complete each sentence.

1. My cat _____was_____ in the garden one day.

2. I _____ sure I saw her wiggle her whiskers.

3. Her whiskers _____ shorter when she was a kitten.

4. A whisker _____ an organ of touch.

5. Whiskers _____ important to a cat.

6. My cat's whiskers _____ very long.

7. Her fur _____ very long, too.

8. I think my cat _____ beautiful!

B. Write There is, There are, There was, or There were to complete each sentence.

1. _____ many kinds of horses.

2. _____ no horses in America at one time.

3. _____ a horse called the pinto that looks painted.

4. _____ many pintos that are famous.

5. _____ pinto horse clubs that you can join today.

6. _____ a national pinto horse club meeting every year.

7. _____ people working to save the pinto horse.

8. _____ a good reason for this—they are beautiful animals.

Subject Pronouns

> - A **pronoun** is a word that takes the place of a noun.
> - A **subject pronoun** is used as the subject of a sentence or as part of the subject of a sentence. The subject pronouns are I, you, he, she, it, we, and they.
>   EXAMPLES: **We** went to class. Shelly and **I** did homework together. **He** is going to help us.

A. Underline the subject pronoun in each sentence.

1. She rode her bike almost every day.
2. It was a beautiful mountain bike.
3. They go as fast as the wind.
4. You can go anywhere on a bike like that.
5. We wanted to ride the bike.
6. I asked for a ride.
7. He got to ride first.
8. Then I got to ride.

B. Complete each sentence by writing a subject pronoun to replace the word or words in parentheses. Pretend you are Bill.

1. Jeff and (Bill) _____I_____ left early for school.
2. (Jeff and I) _____ had a test to study for.
3. (Jeff) _____ had studied, but I hadn't.
4. (The test) _____ was on plants.
5. (Plants) _____ are important to study.
6. "Which part are (Bill) _____ studying?" Jeff asked.
7. (Mrs. Hobart) _____ says this is an important test.
8. (Bill) _____ am going to study hard.

C. Write three sentences of your own using subject pronouns.

1. _____
2. _____
3. _____

Name _____   Date _____

Object Pronouns

> ■ An **object pronoun** is used after an action verb or after words such as to, with, for, and by. The object pronouns are me, you, him, her, it, us, and them.   EXAMPLES: Jim told **him** to start. Alex bought the present for **her.**

A. Underline the object pronoun in each sentence.

1. Jeff won it in record time.

2. The speed of the run surprised us.

3. Jeff beat me by a mile.

4. Maria caught us in the last lap.

5. Wendy will give them the prize.

6. The speech will be made by you.

7. Then a special prize will be given to him.

8. Wendy told me the prize is a blue ribbon.

B. Complete each sentence by writing an object pronoun to replace the word or words in parentheses.

1. The teacher told (I) _____ to read my report.

2. I told (Mr. Sheen) _____ that the report wasn't ready.

3. Mr. Sheen asked when (the report) _____ would be finished.

4. He had warned (our class) _____ that the reports were due.

5. Some of (the reports) _____ were done.

6. A few students offered to read (their reports) _____.

7. The class listened to (Sonja) _____.

8. Mr. Sheen said he wanted (the reports) _____ all finished by Friday.

C. Write four sentences of your own using object pronouns.

1. _____

2. _____

3. _____

4. _____

Using Pronouns

- Remember that a pronoun is a word that takes the place of a noun.
- A subject pronoun is used as the subject of a sentence.
- An object pronoun is used after an action verb, or after words such as <u>to</u>, <u>with</u>, <u>for</u>, and <u>by</u>.
   EXAMPLE: **Sam** gave **the gift** to **the boys. He** gave **it** to **them.**

- **Choose the correct pronoun to replace the underlined nouns in each sentence. Then rewrite each sentence, using the pronoun. You may use a pronoun more than once.**

| He | she | It | him | her | They | them | We | us |

1. <u>Luisa and I</u> decided to attend the talk series at the library.

   _____

2. <u>The talks</u> would be every Wednesday evening for three weeks.

   _____

3. <u>The first one</u> was about the solar system.

   _____

4. We knew we would enjoy all of <u>the talks</u>.

   _____

5. Outer space has always been an interesting topic to <u>Luisa and me</u>.

   _____

6. <u>The professor</u> was an excellent speaker.

   _____

7. The audience listened closely to <u>the speaker</u>.

   _____

8. Luisa said the talk was one of the best <u>Luisa</u> had ever heard.

   _____

9. The new facts we learned surprised <u>Luisa</u>.

   _____

10. In fact, they surprised <u>Luisa and me</u> both.

   _____

Name _____   Date _____

Possessive Pronouns

> ■ A **possessive pronoun** is used to show who or what owns
> something. The possessive pronouns are <u>my</u>, <u>our</u>, <u>your</u>, <u>his</u>,
> <u>her</u>, <u>its</u>, and <u>their</u>.
> EXAMPLES: Is this **your** coat? **His** cold is getting better.

■ **Complete each sentence by writing the correct possessive pronoun.**

1. _____ family and I were going camping.

2. Suddenly _____ car stalled in a dark forest.

3. _____ engine just would not run.

4. _____ family was stuck.

5. Richard almost lost _____ temper.

6. He didn't expect this from _____ car.

7. Julie spoke, and _____ voice made everyone quiet.

8. We held _____ tongues.

9. "_____ hands are trembling," Richard said to Julie.

10. "So are _____ hands," Julie answered.

11. "Look at the bears with _____ paws up in the air," said Julie.

12. Richard tried to start _____ car.

13. Julie held _____ breath while the bears looked at us.

14. The mother bear turned _____ cubs toward the woods.

15. _____ growls could be heard through the car windows.

16. We hid _____ heads below the windows.

17. One cub turned _____ head toward us.

18. I tried to get _____ camera out, but I couldn't.

19. _____ strap was caught on something.

20. "You can tell _____ friends about your adventure when

    we get back," said Richard.

Name _____   Date _____

Adjectives

> ■ An **adjective** is a word that describes a noun. Adjectives tell **which one, what kind,** or **how many.**
> EXAMPLES: **happy** person, **brown** dog, **four** cars

A. Circle the two adjectives in each sentence.

1. The big cat chased the tiny mouse.
2. His sharp teeth flashed in the bright light.
3. The scared mouse ran through the small hole.
4. The speeding cat slipped on the wet floor.
5. The tired mouse hid in a dark corner.
6. The damp cat left in a big hurry.
7. The little mouse had a wide smile.

B. Add an adjective to each sentence in these paragraphs.

beautiful	green	Many	sparkling
fierce	dark	Gentle	Wild

_____ people go to the _____ national parks. They see _____ streams and _____ forests. _____ animals roam freely on _____ meadows. _____ deer and _____ bears both live in the forests.

bare	red	shaky	soft	thick
best	wooden	six	strong	young

The _____ man climbed the _____ ladder. A _____ wind blew the _____ branches. His _____ friend steadied the _____ ladder. He picked _____ _____ apples. The _____ leaves tickled his _____ arm.

Adjectives That Compare

> - Sometimes adjectives are used to compare one thing to another.
> - Most adjectives that compare two things end in -er.
>   EXAMPLE: The red chair is **bigger** than the blue chair.
> - Most adjectives that compare more than two things end in -est.
>   EXAMPLE: That chair is the **biggest** chair in the store.

A. Circle the correct adjective in each sentence.

1. Jean's puppy is the (smaller, smallest) of all the puppies.
2. He is (smaller, smallest) than his brother.
3. Toby was the (cuter, cutest) name Jean could think of.
4. Toby looked (funnier, funniest) than his sister.
5. He had the (whiter, whitest) fur of all the puppies.
6. Toby had the (longer, longest) ears Jean had ever seen.
7. Jean soon learned that Toby was the (naughtier, naughtiest) puppy she had ever known.
8. He played (harder, hardest) than his brother.
9. He stayed awake (later, latest) than his sister.
10. He kept Jean (busier, busiest) than the mother dog.
11. He was the (happier, happiest) puppy in the litter.
12. But he'll never be the (bigger, biggest) dog.

B. Add -er or -est to the end of each adjective to complete the sentences.

1. Tim's hair is light_____ than Jamie's.
2. Who has the dark_____ hair in class?
3. Ida has straight_____ hair than Tina.
4. Tina has the wild_____ hairdo of all.
5. Is her hair long_____ than Jamie's?
6. February is the short_____ month of the year.
7. January is long_____ than June.
8. July is warm_____ than February.
9. March is cold_____ than July.
10. Which do you think is the cold_____ month of all?

Adverbs

> ■ An **adverb** is a word that describes a verb. Adverbs tell
> **how, when,** or **where.** Many adverbs end in -ly.
> EXAMPLES: He ran **quickly.** She was sad **today.**
> Water dripped **here yesterday.**

A. Circle the two adverbs in each sentence.

1. It was widely known that he would cheerfully fix anything.
2. Yesterday he was calmly asked to repair a faucet.
3. He quickly and loudly refused.
4. Later, he quietly apologized for his response.

B. Circle the adverb in each sentence. Then write how, when, or where to show what the adverb tells about the word it describes.

_____ 1. Jim walked quietly.

_____ 2. He sang softly as he walked.

_____ 3. Later, he ate lunch.

_____ 4. He sat there to eat.

C. Use adverbs from the list below to complete the sentences.

anxiously	quickly	Suddenly
brightly	quietly	there
hopelessly	slowly	totally

1. Sam ran _____ to the door.

2. He stood _____ for a minute.

3. _____, Sam ran out the door.

4. The sun shone _____.

5. He looked _____ over his shoulder.

6. He began to walk _____.

7. His quiet day was _____ ruined.

8. He tried _____ to make it to the party on time.

9. Finally, he knocked _____, then joined the party.

Name _____   Date _____

Adverbs That Compare

- **Adverbs,** like adjectives, can be used to compare two or more things.
- Most adverbs that compare two things end in -er.
  EXAMPLE: I arrived **sooner** than you did.
- Most adverbs that compare more than two things end in -est.
  EXAMPLE: Ted runs the **fastest** of all the team members.
- Sometimes more is used with a longer adverb when comparing two things. Sometimes most is used with a longer adverb when comparing more than two things.
  EXAMPLES: I drove **more carefully** than John. Tim drove **most carefully** of all.

A. Circle the correct adverb in each sentence.

1. Jean worked (faster, fastest) than Debbie.

2. Debbie finished (later, latest) than Jean.

3. Of all the workers, Donna worked the (later, latest).

4. She wanted to be done (sooner, soonest) than Jean.

5. Debbie worked (more carefully, most carefully) of all.

6. No one tried (harder, hardest) than Debbie.

B. Complete each sentence by writing the correct form of each adverb in parentheses.

1. The swans arrived (late) _____ than the ducks.

2. Of all the birds, they flew the (quietly) _____.

3. The duck quacked (loudly) _____ than the swan.

4. The swan swam (peacefully) _____ than the duck.

5. The beautiful black swan swam the (near) _____ to me of all the birds.

6. He swam (slowly) _____ than the white swan.

7. I will be back here (soon) _____ than you.

8. The picture of the swans will be taken (carefully) _____ than my other picture.

Using Words Correctly

> ■ Good is an adjective that describes nouns. Well is an adverb that tells how something is done.
>   EXAMPLE: That is a **good** TV that works **well**.

A. Use good or well to complete each sentence.

1. George sings _____, and Jill is a _____ dancer.

2. They work _____ together.

3. Both George and Jill had _____ teachers.

4. They learned _____ from their teachers.

5. They perform their act _____.

6. Their piano music is very _____, too.

7. They both play the piano very _____.

8. Such _____ performers are hard to find.

9. Everyone who sees them perform has a _____ time.

10. I'm going to practice so that I can sing as _____ as George.

11. Don't you think that's a _____ idea?

> ■ Do not use a no word with another no word or after a contraction that ends with -n't. Some no words are no, none, nobody, nothing, nowhere, never, and not.
>   EXAMPLES: Incorrect—**Nobody never** writes me letters.
>   Correct—**Nobody ever** writes me letters.

B. Circle the correct word to complete each sentence.

1. The boy doesn't have (no, any) paper.

2. I haven't (no, any) extra paper for him to borrow.

3. The teacher has (nothing, anything) to give him, either.

4. Doesn't he (ever, never) bring extra paper?

5. Are you sure you don't have (no, any) paper?

6. Hasn't someone got (nothing, anything) to give him?

7. Why doesn't (anybody, nobody) ever plan ahead?

Name _____   Date _____

Using Other Words Correctly

> ■ Those is an adjective used to describe a noun. Them is an
> object pronoun and is used after a verb or a word such as
> at, with, to, and for.
>   EXAMPLES: I like **those** shoes. I'd like to buy **them**.

A. Write them or those to complete each sentence.

1. Did you see _____ boys?

2. I have not seen _____ this afternoon.

3. If I do see _____, I'll give _____ a speech.

4. Have you seen _____ models all over their room?

5. I told _____ to put _____ models away yesterday.

6. I'd better find _____ soon.

7. Otherwise, I might make _____ models disappear!

8. I am not happy with _____ boys at all!

> ■ Doesn't is singular. Use doesn't with one person, place, or thing.
> ■ Don't is plural. Use don't with more than one and with the
> words you and I.
>   EXAMPLES: Ed **doesn't** have a ride home. We **don't** have
>   room in the car.

B. Write doesn't or don't to complete each sentence.

1. Juan and Charles _____ want to miss the practice.

2. Charles _____ like to be late.

3. Juan thinks it _____ matter if they're late.

4. Jamie _____ seem to care if he goes to practice.

5. Juan and Charles _____ understand why he _____ want to go.

6. The coach _____ want anyone to miss a practice.

7. He says they can't win if they _____ practice.

8. I _____ doubt that for a minute.

Name _____ Date _____

Unit 3 Test

Choose the correct plural form of each underlined singular noun.

1. country
   - **A** ○ countreys
   - **B** ○ countrys
   - **C** ○ countries
   - **D** ○ country's

2. box
   - **A** ○ boxys
   - **B** ○ boxs
   - **C** ○ boxies
   - **D** ○ boxes

3. calf
   - **A** ○ calfs
   - **B** ○ calvs
   - **C** ○ calves
   - **D** ○ calfies

4. woman
   - **A** ○ women
   - **B** ○ womyn
   - **C** ○ wimmin
   - **D** ○ woman's

Choose the phrase that shows the correct possessive for each underlined phrase.

5. the hat of my father
   - **A** ○ the hat's of my father
   - **B** ○ my fathers' hat
   - **C** ○ my father's hats
   - **D** ○ my father's hat

6. the pages of the book
   - **A** ○ the book's pages'
   - **B** ○ the books' pages
   - **C** ○ the book page's
   - **D** ○ the book's pages

Choose the sentence that has an action verb.

7. **A** ○ Rain is water.
   - **B** ○ Rain falls from the sky.
   - **C** ○ Rain feels soft on my face.
   - **D** ○ Rain had been expected.

8. **A** ○ Lee kicked the ball.
   - **B** ○ Lee feels tired.
   - **C** ○ Lee is thirsty.
   - **D** ○ Lee became sleepy.

Choose the sentence that has a linking verb.

9. **A** ○ We had been waiting.
   - **B** ○ We grew impatient.
   - **C** ○ We called the number.
   - **D** ○ We asked for George.

10. **A** ○ Erin is talented.
    - **B** ○ Erin wants to be a star.
    - **C** ○ Erin sings and dances.
    - **D** ○ Erin even tells jokes.

Choose the sentence that has a helping verb.

11. **A** ○ Dirk has gone for help.
    - **B** ○ Dirk seemed sad.
    - **C** ○ Dirk pulled his jacket on.
    - **D** ○ Dirk walked away.

12. **A** ○ I accepted an invitation.
    - **B** ○ It sounded like fun.
    - **C** ○ I looked at my calendar.
    - **D** ○ I am going tomorrow.

Choose the correct verb to complete each sentence.

13. Regina and Tony _____ cousins.

   A ○ are   C ○ was

   B ○ is   D ○ am

14. Todd and I _____ each other.

   A ○ seen   C ○ saw

   B ○ has seen   D ○ have saw

15. You already _____ me some.

   A ○ have gave   C ○ given

   B ○ gave   D ○ give

16. They _____ each other every summer.

   A ○ sees   C ○ visiting

   B ○ visits   D ○ visit

17. When will you _____ her again?

   A ○ had seen   C ○ see

   B ○ seen   D ○ saw

18. I _____ to visit you.

   A ○ have came   C ○ had coming

   B ○ came   D ○ coming

Choose the correct pronoun to complete each sentence.

19. _____ runs in many races.

   A ○ We   B ○ Him   C ○ He   D ○ I

20. All of _____ grapes were ripe.

   A ○ mine   B ○ him   C ○ them   D ○ my

21. We told _____.

   A ○ they   B ○ them   C ○ he   D ○ she

22. _____ heel was broken.

   A ○ Her   B ○ She   C ○ Them   D ○ Our

23. That looks like _____ son.

   A ○ its   B ○ them   C ○ their   D they

Choose the correct adjective or adverb to complete each sentence.

24. The giraffe is the _____ animal.

   A ○ tall   B ○ taller   C ○ tallest D ○ tallness

25. The blue whale is _____ than any other mammal.

   A ○ biggest   B ○ big   C ○ bigly   D ○ bigger

26. She plays the piano very _____.

   A ○ good   B ○ better   C ○ well   D ○ best

27. Don't you have _____ family?

   A ○ any   B ○ no   C ○ none   D ○ no one

28. The phone rang _____.

   A ○ sudden B ○ loud   C ○ suddenly D ○ jarring

Name _____   Date _____

Capitalizing Names of People and Pets

> ■ **Capitalize** the names of people and pets.
>   EXAMPLES: Laura Ingalls Wilder wrote many stories.
>   Did she have a lamb named Cotton?
> ■ Capitalize family names.
>   EXAMPLES: Uncle Bob married Aunt Margie.
>   Mom and Dad got married in California.

■ **Rewrite these sentences using capital letters where needed.**

1. uncle george got up early today.

_____

2. He and aunt beth had a special job to do.

_____

3. uncle george and aunt beth were going to the animal shelter.

_____

4. They wanted to find a puppy for susan and michael.

_____

5. uncle george and aunt beth thought a small dog would be nice.

_____

6. But susan and michael wanted a big dog.

_____

7. uncle george saw a cute kitten named mittens.

_____

8. In the very last cage, they saw sasha.

_____

9. uncle george and aunt beth loved her at once.

_____

10. When sasha ran circles around michael, he loved her, too.

_____

Unit 4, Capitalization and Punctuation
© Steck-Vaughn Publishing Company

60

Language Practice 4, SV 7160-0

Capitalizing Names of Places and Things

> - Capitalize each word in a place name.
>   EXAMPLES: Chicago, Germany, Utah, Howard School,
>   Main Library, Missouri River
> - Capitalize days of the week, months of the year, holidays,
>   and names of monuments.
>   EXAMPLES: Tuesday, February, Valentine's Day,
>   the Lincoln Memorial

A. Rewrite these sentences using capital letters where needed.

1. Our family will spend memorial day in washington.

   _____

2. We hope to see the white house and the washington monument.

   _____

3. We also want to see the smithsonian institution.

   _____

4. The potomac river forms a border between
   washington and virginia.

   _____

5. The lincoln memorial is amazing to see at night.

   _____

6. The vietnam memorial gets many visitors.

   _____

7. There are many amazing sights in washington.

   _____

B. Answer these questions. Use capital letters where needed.

1. When were you born?

   _____

2. What is your address? Include the city and state.

   _____

3. What is your favorite holiday?

   _____

Capitalizing Titles

> ■ Capitalize the first, last, and all important words in a book title. Words such as a, an, and, but, by, for, in, of, on, from, the, and to are not considered important words. They are not capitalized unless one of them is the first word in the title. Underline all titles of books.
>   EXAMPLE: A Present from Rosita
> ■ Capitalize titles of respect.
>   EXAMPLES: Major Thomas, Doctor Freeman

A. Rewrite these names and titles correctly. Underline the book titles.

1. doctor william h. black _____

2. judge rosa allen _____

3. The book: a wrinkle in time _____

4. captain william faircroft _____

5. The president of the united states _____

6. doctor laurie c. bell _____

7. The book: attack of the monster plants _____

8. major carol gates _____

9. The book: owls in the family _____

10. The book: my side of the mountain _____

B. Circle each letter that should be capitalized. Write the capital letter above it. Underline the book titles.

1. The results of mr. thomas's plan are interesting.

2. He wrote to judge george king and asked for his help
   in finding people to speak at our school.

3. judge king got judge claire booth to speak about her
   book, life in the courts.

4. So ms. dias told us to read life in the courts before judge booth spoke.

5. Another suggested book is a judge's story by raymond field.

Name _____ Date _____

Capitalizing Abbreviations

> - Capitalize **abbreviations** of days and months.
>   EXAMPLES: Sun., Mon., Tues., Wed., Thurs., Fri., Sat.
>   November—Nov., August—Aug.
> - Capitalize abbreviations for titles of respect.
>   EXAMPLES: Mr., Mrs., Dr.
> - Capitalize an **initial,** the first letter of a name.
>   EXAMPLE: T. J. Woodhouse

A. Write the correct abbreviation for the days and months of the year.

1. Tuesday _____

2. Wednesday _____

3. Thursday _____

4. Friday _____

5. Saturday _____

6. Sunday _____

7. January _____

8. November _____

9. September _____

10. August _____

11. October _____

12. December _____

B. Rewrite these sentences using capital letters where needed.

1. The conference is planned for aug. 12.

   _____

2. It will be held in wm. Taft Park.

   _____

3. George w. Bush will be there.

   _____

4. Our mayor, ms. Foster, was pleased he could come.

   _____

5. Police Chief e. s. Rodriguez will introduce him.

   _____

6. Many people want to hear mr. Bush speak.

   _____

7. They want to know how he likes life away from Washington, d. c.

   _____

Capitalizing Parts of a Letter

- Capitalize the street name, city, and date in a letter. Also capitalize all letters in abbreviations for states. Together these words make up the **heading.**
  EXAMPLE: 1100 N. Main St.
  　　　　　Hartford, CT 06105
  　　　　　May 24, 19__
- Capitalize the **greeting.**
  EXAMPLE: Dear Mr. Jones,
- Capitalize the first word of the **closing.**
  EXAMPLES: Sincerely yours, Your friend,

■ **Underline the letters that should be capitalized in the letters.**

7216 melvin street
houston, tx 77040
october 23, 19__

dear fred,

　I am doing a report on farm life. Do you have any information you can send me? My report must be turned in three weeks from today. I can really use any help you can give me. Pictures and facts would be helpful. The names of some books I could find at the library would also help a lot.

　　　　　　　　your friend,
　　　　　　　　jesse

820 w. state st.
lockhart, al 36455
october 29, 19__

dear jesse,

　I'll be glad to help with your report. Better yet, why don't you come and visit? Call and let me know if you are coming. The library here serves all of alabama. I know we could find all the information you need.

　　　　　　　　your friend,
　　　　　　　　fred

Capitalizing and Punctuating Sentences

- Begin all sentences with a capital letter.
  EXAMPLE: Mary rode a bike.
- End a statement or a command with a **period. (.)**
  EXAMPLE: Jake rode a bike.
- End a question with a **question mark. (?)**
  EXAMPLE: Did Jake ride a bike?
- End an exclamation with an **exclamation point. (!)**
  EXAMPLE: Ouch, I fell!

A. Begin and end each sentence correctly. Put the correct punctuation mark at the end of each sentence, and circle any letters that should be capitalized.

1. i am going to ride my bike to the store

2. where is my bike

3. it is always in the garage by the hose

4. could it be on the back porch

5. i'll ask Joanne if she has seen it

6. she said it was in the garage this morning

7. oh, no, someone has stolen my bike

8. what should I do now

9. who could have taken it

B. Rewrite each sentence correctly.

1. i'll call the police about my bike

_____

2. hurry, hurry, answer the phone

_____

3. hello, is this the police station

_____

4. yes, what can we do for you

_____

5. you must help me catch a bike thief

_____

6. how do you know your bike wasn't borrowed

_____

Using Commas in Sentences

> ■ Use a **comma** (,) to take the place of the word and when three or more things are listed together in a sentence.
>   EXAMPLE: Mary, Pete, and George went to the beach.
> ■ Use a comma to separate the parts of a compound sentence.
>   EXAMPLE: Mary drove her car, but Peter walked.
> ■ Use a comma to set off words such as yes, no, and well at the beginning of a sentence.
>   EXAMPLE: Yes, I want to ride my bike.

■ **Rewrite these sentences using commas correctly. Leave out the word and when possible.**

1. I called Juan and Janet and Karen last Saturday.

_____

2. Yes they wanted to have a picnic.

_____

3. Juan packed a lunch and Karen brought a backpack.

_____

4. Well we were finally ready to go.

_____

5. Yes we found a perfect place by the beach.

_____

6. We played volleyball and swam and hiked.

_____

7. It was a great picnic and there were no ants around.

_____

8. We collected shells and driftwood and pebbles.

_____

9. Juan cleaned up the garbage and Karen packed the leftovers.

_____

10. We sang and laughed and read.

_____

Using Commas in Other Sentences

- Use a comma to set off the name of a person spoken to.
  EXAMPLE: Pam, you said we could go.
- Use commas to set off a phrase that helps explain the subject of a sentence.
  EXAMPLE: Mr. Gonzales, Rudy's father, is a lawyer.

A. Add commas where needed in each sentence.

1. Our neighbor Buddy Rush is gone.
2. Mr. Rush his father said he doesn't know where Buddy is.
3. Danny did Buddy talk about going somewhere?
4. This seems very strange to me Tim.
5. Chief Carter our sheriff thinks so, too.
6. Buddy where are you?
7. Danny don't you remember what I told you?
8. What should we do now Chief Carter?

B. Put an X in front of the sentence that tells about each numbered sentence.

1. Craig, your brother is here.

   _____ Craig is your brother.

   _____ Someone is talking to Craig.

2. Lydia, my friend will go, too.

   _____ Lydia is my friend.

   _____ Someone is talking to Lydia.

3. Our neighbor, Mrs. Hicks, is sick.

   _____ Mrs. Hicks is our neighbor.

   _____ Someone is talking to your neighbor.

4. Carrie, your sister is home.

   _____ Carrie is your sister.

   _____ Someone is talking to Carrie.

5. Anna, my dog, is loose.

   _____ Anna is my dog.

   _____ Someone is talking to Anna.

Name _____ Date _____

Using Commas in Letters

> - Use a comma between the city and state in the heading. Use a comma between the day and year.
>   EXAMPLE: 872 Park Street
>   Chicago, IL 60641
>   September 17, 19__
> - Use a comma following the name in the greeting.
>   EXAMPLES: Dear Nancy, Dear Mr. Muller,
> - Use a comma following the last word of the closing.
>   EXAMPLES: Sincerely yours, Your friend,

A. Add commas where needed in the letters.

                                422 W. South St.
                                Dallas TX 72843
                                November 12 19__

Dear Mark

   Thank you for coming to my party. It was fun having you there. I also want to thank you for the great sweatshirt. It fits fine, and I really like it.

                                Your friend
                                Theresa

_____

                                8200 Columbus Ave.
                                Dallas TX 72844
                                November 16 19__

Dear Theresa

   Don't forget about the trip to the museum on Saturday. See you there.
                                Sincerely
                                Mark

B. Add commas where they are needed in the headings.

1. 321 Pebble Beach Drive
   Jacksonville FL 32211
   November 17 19__

2. 101 Main St.
   Oakland CA 10032
   July 10 19__

C. Add commas where they are needed in the greetings and closings.

1. Dear Juana

2. Sincerely yours

3. Your friend

4. Dear Grandmother

5. Your grandson

6. Hi, Scott

Using Quotation Marks

> ■ A **quote** tells the exact words someone says. Put **quotation marks** (" ") before and after the words. Use a comma, a period, a question mark, or an exclamation point between the quoted words and the rest of the sentence. Begin the first word of a direct quote with a capital letter.
>
> EXAMPLES: "Why don't you eat your cereal?" asked Jack.
> Jenny said, "I'm not hungry."

■ **Look at the pictures. See who is talking and what is being said. Tell what each speaker said. Include the word <u>said</u> or <u>asked</u> and the name of the speaker. Add quotation marks and commas where needed.**

Do you want to talk about the interesting places we each visited this summer?

Ms. Chen

My sister and I visited my aunt in Nome, Alaska.

James

We flew to Quebec to see our grandmother.

Jenny

We went to Arizona and saw the Grand Canyon.

Richard

1. What did Ms. Chen say?

   "Do you want to talk about the interesting places we each

   visited this summer?" asked Ms. Chen.

2. What did James say?

   _____

3. What did Jenny say?

   _____

4. What did Richard say?

   _____

More About Quotation Marks

- Sometimes the speaker of a quote is named in the middle of the words being spoken. When this happens, quotation marks should be placed before and after both groups of words. Commas are placed inside the quotation marks at the end of the first group of words and again after the speaker's name.
  EXAMPLE: "I'd like to go," said Mary, "but I can't."

- **Place quotation marks around the quotes. Add question marks and commas where needed.**

1. Well said Mike Dot is just getting over a strange accident.

2. What happened asked Susan.

3. A thought struck her said Mike.

4. Jake asked Why did you throw the alarm clock out the window

5. Because said Joan I wanted to see time fly.

6. What did one wall say to another asked Bonnie.

7. I'll meet you at the corner answered David.

8. What gets wetter Carlos asked the more you dry

9. A towel does said Angie.

10. Mother said Are your feet dirty

11. Yes replied Bobby but don't worry because I have my shoes on.

12. Maria asked How can you tell when an ice cube is nervous

13. It breaks out said Bill in a cold sweat.

14. Anna asked What is black-and-white and red all over

15. It's a blushing zebra said Jake.

16. What did the rug say to the floor asked Mike.

17. Don't move replied Bonnie because I've got you covered.

18. Joan asked Why do sponges do a good job

19. They become absorbed in their work said Carlos.

20. Angie asked Why is a pencil like a riddle

21. Because said Maria it's no good without a point.

Name _____   Date _____

Using Apostrophes in Contractions

> - Use an **apostrophe** (') in a contraction to show where a letter or letters are taken out.
> - <u>Won't</u> is an exception. will not = won't
> - Contractions can be made by joining a verb and <u>not</u>.
>   EXAMPLES: can not = can't, did not = didn't
> - Contractions can also be made by joining a noun or pronoun and a verb.
>   EXAMPLES: **It's** (it + is) a beautiful day.
>   **Susan's** (Susan + is) going to the park.
>   **She'll** (she + will) have a lot of fun.

A. Circle the correct meaning for the contraction in each sentence.

1. Donna said she'll go to the store today.   (she will, she had)
2. We're supposed to clean the house.   (We will, We are)
3. Beth and James say they'll clean the living room, too.
   (they will, they would)
4. I'll clean the kitchen.   (I would, I will)
5. She's going to be home soon.   (She is, She will)
6. We'd better get moving!   (We will, We had)

B. Write the contraction for the underlined words.

1. <u>It is</u> funny that <u>we are</u> lost.

_____   _____

2. <u>You are</u> sure <u>we have</u> followed the directions correctly?

_____   _____

3. <u>I am</u> sure <u>they will</u> start looking for us soon.

_____   _____

4. We <u>did not</u> bring a map, but we <u>should have</u>.

_____   _____

5. <u>I will</u> bet that <u>we will</u> be here all night.

_____   _____

6. <u>We are</u> in trouble now because <u>I am</u> tired.

_____   _____

Using Apostrophes to Show Possession

> ■ Remember that apostrophes are not only used in contractions.
> They are also used to show ownership, or possession.
> EXAMPLES: Contraction—My **sister's** coming here.
> Possessive—My **sister's** friend is coming here. Both
> my **sisters'** friends are coming.

A. Rewrite each word in parentheses to show ownership. Use -'s or -s'.

1. Our family went on a picnic in my (brother) _____ car.

2. The (car) _____ windows would not roll down.

3. (Dad) _____ clothes were soaked with sweat.

4. Both my (sisters) _____ jeans were wrinkled.

5. Finally my (family) _____ terrible trip was over.

6. We arrived at our (friends) _____ house for our picnic.

**B. Rewrite each sentence. Replace each underlined phrase with a phrase
that includes a possessive with an apostrophe.**

1. We all liked the story Jennifer told the best.

   _____

2. The setting of the story was an old castle.

   _____

3. There was a prison in the basement of the castle.

   _____

4. The attention of the students was on Jennifer as she read.

   _____

5. A cruel man lived in the tower of the castle.

   _____

6. The children of the cruel man weren't allowed to play.

   _____

72

Unit 4 Test

Choose the correct answer to each question.

In which sentence are the words capitalized correctly?

1. A ○ Rebecca likes people.
  B ○ She has many Friends.
  C ○ Her friends Like her.
  D ○ Rebecca is a Computer Operator.

2. A ○ The empire state building is tall.
  B ○ It Looms over New York city.
  C ○ you can go up to the top.
  D ○ Can you see the Atlantic Ocean?

3. A ○ The Lawyer made a joke.
  B ○ Judge hardy laughed.
  C ○ The judge's dog, Ripper, growled.
  D ○ Judge Hardy told ripper to be quiet.

Which sentence is written correctly?

4. A ○ "Mary will you show us the pictures
  B ○ Sure, said Mary I'll be glad to.
  C ○ "These are great," Alice said.
  D ○ "It was a lot of fun" said Mary

5. A ○ "Let me go, said Eileen.
  B ○ Chuck said, "I'll come, too.
  C ○ "I want to be alone," she said.
  D ○ Okay, said Chuck.

Which sentence needs a comma?

6. A ○ Sue came home on Friday.
  B ○ She was tired but she was happy.
  C ○ Everyone was glad to see her.
  D ○ They planned a party for her.

7. A ○ He was tired so he took a nap.
  B ○ He slept all afternoon.
  C ○ He snored and dreamed.
  D ○ He remembered his dream.

Which greeting is written correctly?

8. A ○ dear Tina,
  B ○ Dear Tina
  C ○ Dear Ms. Jones
  D ○ Dear Ms. Jones,

9. A ○ dear marsha,
  B ○ Dear Marsha,
  C ○ Dear marsha
  D ○ Dear Marsha

Which closing is written correctly?

10. A ○ Sincerely yours,
  B ○ Sincerely Yours,
  C ○ Sincerely yours
  D ○ sincerely yours,

11. A ○ yours truly,
  B ○ Yours truly,
  C ○ Yours truly
  D ○ your's Truly,

12. Which address is written correctly?
  A ○ 4700 w greenwood
    Park Ridge, il 60030
  B ○ 1023 North lamar
    austin, TX 78767
  C ○ 7280 N. Martin
    Boulder, CO 72815
  D ○ 871 W. Oak
    Boston Ma 01340

Choose the sentence that is punctuated correctly.

13. **A** ○ Will help.

   B ○ Would you like to sit here.

   C ○ Where are you going?

   D ○ How are you!

14. **A** ○ Don't cut yourself!

   B ○ Is it sharp.

   C ○ Very sharp.

   D ○ I'll be careful?

Choose the two words that make each underlined contraction.

15. we're

   A ○ we will   **C** ○ we would

   B ○ we have   **D** ○ we are

16. it's

   A ○ it is   **C** ○ it did

   B ○ it was   **D** ○ it will

Choose the phrase in which the apostrophe is used correctly.

17. **A** ○ didn't know how

   B ○ the meetings members

   C ○ lets' go

   D ○ it's leg

18. **A** ○ Helens' daughter

   B ○ was'nt there

   C ○ lost shoe's

   D ○ farmer's cattle

19. **A** ○ do'nt worry

   B ○ his money's worth

   C ○ shouldnt' care

   D ○ Lizs' address

Choose the sentence that needs a capital letter.

20. **A** ○ Sara was on vacation.

   B ○ She went to mt. Rushmore.

   C ○ She studied its history.

   D ○ Mt. Rushmore is very famous.

21. **A** ○ Abraham Lincoln is one of the faces.

   B ○ Abe is famous, too.

   C ○ He was president of the united states.

   D ○ President Lincoln was a kind man.

Choose the two words that make each underlined contraction.

22. I'm

   A ○ I will   **C** ○ I am

   B ○ I would   **D** ○ I have

23. won't

   A ○ would not   **C** ○ do not

   B ○ did not   **D** ○ will not

Choose the phrase in which the apostrophe is used correctly.

24. **A** ○ couldn't find it

   B ○ that beaches' sand

   C ○ times' flying

   D ○ going to Wesleys'

25. **A** ○ flie's wings

   B ○ up in arms'

   C ○ Marias' car

   D ○ boxes' lids

26. **A** ○ countrie's flag

   B ○ they'll stay

   C ○ is'nt gone

   D ○ up the stair's

Name _____ Date _____

Writing Sentences

> ■ Remember that a **sentence** is a group of words that tells a complete thought.
> ■ A sentence must have at least two parts—a subject and a predicate.
>
>   S   P
>   EXAMPLE: <u>Nora Vargas</u> <u>was bored</u>.

■ **Read each group of words. Then answer the questions.**

1. Nora needed a hobby.

  a. Is there a subject? _____   If so, what is it? _____

  b. Is there a predicate? _____   If so, what is it? _____

  c. Is there a complete thought? _____   Is this a sentence? _____

2. Nora finally.

  a. Is there a subject? _____   If so, what is it? _____

  b. Is there a predicate? _____   If so, what is it? _____

  c. Is there a complete thought? _____   Is this a sentence? _____

3. Will do a family history.

  a. Is there a subject? _____   If so, what is it? _____

  b. Is there a predicate? _____   If so, what is it? _____

  c. Is there a complete thought? _____   Is this a sentence? _____

4. Nora began planning.

  a. Is there a subject? _____   If so, what is it? _____

  b. Is there a predicate? _____   If so, what is it? _____

  c. Is there a complete thought? _____   Is this a sentence? _____

5. Asked questions.

  a. Is there a subject? _____   If so, what is it? _____

  b. Is there a predicate? _____   If so, what is it? _____

  c. Is there a complete thought? _____   Is this a sentence? _____

Writing Topic Sentences

- A **paragraph** is a group of sentences about one main idea. There are usually several sentences in a paragraph. But sometimes a paragraph is only one sentence long. The first line of a paragraph is indented.
- A **topic sentence** is a sentence that tells the main idea of a paragraph. The topic sentence is usually the first sentence in a paragraph.

A. Read the paragraph. Underline the topic sentence.

    Nora decided that she needed a hobby. She thought about different things to pick for a hobby. She thought about collecting coins or stamps. Nora finally chose to do a family history as her hobby.

B. Rewrite the sentences below in paragraph form. Put the topic sentence first and underline it. Remember to indent the first sentence.

1. To get the information she needed, Nora would have to ask many questions.
2. She thought about the kinds of questions she would ask.
3. She wanted to make sure that she didn't forget any questions.
4. So Nora wrote down a list of questions that she would ask each person.
5. Next she made copies of the list.
6. She put one person's name at the top of each copy.
7. Then she was ready to talk to people.

_____

_____

_____

_____

_____

_____

_____

_____

Writing Supporting Details

> ■ Sentences with **supporting details** give more information about the main idea of a paragraph. Each sentence should contain details that support the topic sentence.

■ **Three sentences do not support the topic sentence. Draw a line through them. Then write the topic sentence and the five supporting sentences in paragraph form. Remember to indent the first sentence.**

   Topic Sentence: Nora was ready to begin her history.

1. First, she put her questions into a notebook.
2. She made sure she had pens and extra paper.
3. Then Nora called Grandpa Casey and asked when she could come and talk to him.
4. She told Grandpa Casey about her new dog.
5. Grandpa Casey is fun.
6. She also called Grandpa Vargas.
7. Both of her grandfathers were glad to help with the family history.
8. Many of Nora's friends had hobbies.

_____

_____

_____

_____

_____

_____

_____

_____

_____

_____

Name _____   Date _____

Using Time Order in Paragraphs

> ■ **Time order** is used to tell things in the order in which they happened. Some words that help show time order are <u>first</u>, <u>next</u>, <u>then</u>, <u>afterward</u>, and <u>finally</u>.

■ **Number the sentences below in the order in which the events happened. Place the topic sentence first. Then write the sentences in paragraph form. Remember to indent the first sentence.**

_____   1. He took a train from Canada to Boston.

_____   2. He worked in Chicago for three years.

_____   3. Casey came a long way on his journey to Sacramento.

_____   4. First, he traveled by coach to Dublin, Ireland.

_____   5. Finally, he left Chicago and drove to Sacramento.

_____   6. After working for five years in Boston, he took a bus to Chicago.

_____   7. Then he took a ship from Ireland to Canada.

_____   8. He lived in Canada for two years.

_____   9. He stayed in Dublin for only two months.

_____   10. Now he enjoys telling about the cities he has lived in.

_____

_____

_____

_____

_____

_____

_____

_____

_____

_____

Writing a Conversation

- When writing a **conversation**, be sure to:
  - Use quotation marks around each quote.
  - Use words such as <u>said</u> and <u>asked</u> with each quote.
  - Begin a new paragraph for each quote.
    EXAMPLES: Nora asked, "Will you tell me about your childhood?"
    Grandpa said, "Of course I will."

- **Rewrite the paragraph as a conversation between Nora and Grandpa Vargas. Be sure to start a new paragraph for each quote.**

    Nora asked Grandpa Vargas what it was like when he was growing up. Grandpa Vargas said he would tell her about his boyhood in Mexico. He said that his father raised sheep. He said that he used to watch the flock of sheep for his father. Grandpa said it was not an easy job because wolves were always nearby. Nora asked Grandpa Vargas to tell her about the wolves.

Nora asked, "What was it like when you were growing up?"

_____

_____

_____

_____

_____

_____

_____

_____

_____

_____

_____

_____

Topic and Audience

> - The **topic** is the subject you are writing about. The topic of a paragraph or story should be something that interests you.
> - The **audience** is the person or people who will read what you wrote. Before starting to write, ask yourself some questions: Who will read this? How old are the people who will read this? What kinds of things are they interested in?

A. Next to the list of topics, write <u>adult</u>, <u>teenager</u>, or <u>child</u> to show who might be most interested in the topic.

_____ 1. A story about the amount of gas different car models use

_____ 2. A picture book about baby animals

_____ 3. A story about dirt-bike racing

_____ 4. A travel story about Spain

_____ 5. Nursery rhymes

_____ 6. A story about a rock group's travels

_____ 7. A story about teenage movie stars

_____ 8. Fairy tales

_____ 9. The life story of a famous writer

_____ 10. A book of riddles

_____ 11. A book about home remodeling

B. Write five topics that are interesting. Then write the audience that you think might be interested in each topic.

Topic	Audience
1. _____	_____
2. _____	_____
3. _____	_____
4. _____	_____
5. _____	_____

Name _____   Date _____

Planning an Outline

- An **outline** is a plan to help organize writing. An outline lists the main ideas of a topic.
- An outline starts with a **statement** that tells the topic of the writing. The statement is followed by **main headings** and **subheadings** that tell what goes into each part. Main headings start with a roman numeral. Subheadings start with a capital letter.

Statement: Grandpa Vargas's life

(Main Heading)   I. Childhood
                A. Born in Mexico
(Subheadings)   B. Moved to the U.S.
          II. Adult Years
                A. Worked in factory
                B. Started grocery store

- **Choose one of your topics from page 80. Write an outline for that topic. Use the sample outline as a guide.**

Statement: _____

    I. _____

        A. _____

        B. _____

    II. _____

        A. _____

        B. _____

    III. _____

        A. _____

        B. _____

    IV. _____

        A. _____

        B. _____

A Narrative Paragraph

> ■ A **narrative paragraph** tells a story. A narrative paragraph usually tells events in the order in which they happened.

■ **Read the model paragraph. Then follow the directions.**

"Ah," said Grandpa, "my meeting with the wolf was very exciting. We had just arrived at the meadow. This day, the sheep would not settle down. Blanco, my dog, was acting strangely, too. He kept circling the sheep, trying to keep them in a tight group. Suddenly, Blanco leaped on the back of one sheep and raced across the flock, back by back. Then, from a bunch of bushes, raced a huge gray form. 'Wolf!' my mind screamed, 'Wolf!' Blanco reached the edge of the flock just as the wolf did. Without slowing down, Blanco threw himself at the wolf. Next, I grabbed a stick and ran toward the wolf. I yelled and yelled and swung with the stick. I don't think I really ever touched the wolf. I was too scared to aim. Finally, I think he just got tired of all the noise we were making. He turned and trotted away. He didn't run, though. He made sure we knew that he wasn't afraid of us. Afterward, Blanco and I were very proud of ourselves."

1. Underline the topic sentence, and circle the time order words.
2. List the events of the story in the proper time order and in your own words.

   1. They had just arrived at the meadow.

   _____

   _____

   _____

   _____

   _____

   _____

   _____

   _____

   _____

Name _____ Date _____

Writing a Narrative Paragraph

To write a narrative paragraph, follow these steps:
- Choose a topic, or subject.
- Decide who your audience will be.
- Write a topic sentence.
- Add supporting details.
- Use time order words to help the reader know when the events happened.

- **Choose a topic for a narrative paragraph. Write a topic sentence that will be the first sentence of your paragraph. Then add supporting sentences to complete the paragraph.**

Topic: _____

Topic Sentence: _____

_____

Paragraph:

_____

_____

_____

_____

_____

_____

_____

_____

_____

_____

_____

_____

_____

Unit 5 Test

Read the paragraphs. Then answer the questions.

A

Vince had a plan. First, he would get a job. Then he would save all his money. Next, he would buy a car. Vince's brother has a car.

1. What is the topic sentence in paragraph A?

- **A** ○ Vince had a plan.
- **B** ○ First, he would get a job.
- **C** ○ Then he would save all his money.
- **D** ○ Next, he would buy a car.

2. Which sentence in paragraph A does not give supporting details?

- **A** ○ Then, he would save all his money.
- **B** ○ First, he would get a job.
- **C** ○ Next, he would buy a car.
- **D** ○ Vince's brother has a car.

3. Which form of punctuation is used around a quote, in all paragraphs?

- **A** ○ periods
- **B** ○ commas
- **C** ○ quotation marks
- **D** ○ question marks

B

The plan had some problems. Vince didn't make enough money. Cars are all very expensive. He bought a gift with his money. Vince's birthday was last week.

4. What is the topic sentence in paragraph B?

- **A** ○ The plan had some problems.
- **B** ○ Vince didn't make enough money.
- **C** ○ Cars are all very expensive.
- **D** ○ He bought a gift with his money.

5. Which sentence in paragraph B does not give supporting details?

- **A** ○ Vince didn't make enough money.
- **B** ○ Cars are all very expensive.
- **C** ○ He bought a gift with his money.
- **D** ○ Vince's birthday was last week.

6. What should you consider when writing a paragraph?

- **A** ○ only your interests
- **B** ○ when it will be read
- **C** ○ books you've read lately
- **D** ○ the audience

Choose the time order word from each sentence.

7. Then he saved money.

- **A** ○ he   **C** ○ Then
- **B** ○ money   **D** ○ saved

8. Finally, he got to buy a car.

- **A** ○ Finally   **C** ○ car
- **B** ○ buy   **D** ○ got

9. Afterward, he said goodbye.

- **A** ○ Afterward **C** ○ said
- **B** ○ he   **D** ○ goodbye

10. Next, he will save for clothes.

- **A** ○ save   **C** ○ clothes
- **B** ○ Next   **D** ○ for

Name _____ Date _____

Read the conversation. Then answer the questions.

I don't know what to do, said José.
"What's the problem" asked Lonny.
José said, "I can't decide whether to go to the movie or to the race. They both sound like fun."
"Why don't you go to the movie tomorrow? Surely it will be playing then."
"That is a great idea!"

11. What punctuation is missing from the first sentence?

A ○ question mark

B ○ exclamation point

C ○ quotation marks

D ○ comma

12. Who says the movie and the race sound like fun?

A ○ José   C ○ I

B ○ Lonny   D ○ They

13. What is the simple subject of the first sentence?

A ○ José   C ○ what

B ○ I   D ○ do

14. What punctuation should come after the word "problem"?

A ○ comma

B ○ question mark

C ○ period

D ○ exclamation point

15. Who says going to the movie tomorrow is a great idea?

A ○ José   C ○ I

B ○ Lonny   D ○ They

16. What is the simple predicate of the last sentence?

A ○ idea   C ○ great

B ○ that   D ○ is

Study the following outline. Then answer the questions.

Statement: Saving natural resources

I. Problems

  A. Pollution

    1. air

    2.

    3. land

  B.

    1. food

    2. paper

    3.

    4. plastics

II. Solutions

  A. Conservation

  B.

17. What best fits as subheading I. A. 2.?

A ○ wastes   C ○ garbage

B ○ oil   D ○ water

18. What best fits as subheading I. B.?

A ○ Oceans   C ○ Deserts

B ○ Rain Forests   D ○ Wastes

19. What best fits as subheading I. B. 3.?

A ○ plants   C ○ glass

B ○ doors   D ○ toys

20. What best fits as subheading II. B.?

A ○ Recycling   C ○ Burying

B ○ Piling   D ○ Burning

Alphabetical Order

- **Alphabetical order** is often used to organize names or words on a list. Use the first letter of each word to put the words in the order of the alphabet.
- If two words begin with the same letter, look at the second letter to see which would come first.   EXAMPLE: **fan, fine**
- If the first and second letters are the same, look at the third letter.   EXAMPLE: **fine, fire**

- **Read the groups of topics below.**
Number the terms in each group in alphabetical order.

1. homonyms _____

synonyms _____

antonyms _____

suffixes _____

prefixes _____

contractions _____

vocabulary _____

opposites _____

2. index _____

accent _____

pronunciation _____

definitions _____

alphabetical _____

dictionaries _____

respellings _____

titles _____

copyright _____

3. statements _____

sentences _____

commands _____

subjects _____

predicates _____

exclamations _____

questions _____

run-ons _____

4. capitalization _____

punctuation _____

abbreviations _____

initials _____

quotes _____

commas _____

closing _____

greeting _____

periods _____

5. adjectives _____

nouns _____

verbs _____

adverbs _____

pronouns _____

apostrophes _____

possessives _____

tenses _____

6. topics _____

paragraphs _____

details _____

conversations _____

sentences _____

titles _____

narrative _____

audience _____

outlines _____

Name _____   Date _____

Dictionary: Guide Words

> ■ **Guide words** are at the top of each page in a dictionary.
> Guide words tell the first and last words listed on each
> page. Every word listed on the page comes between the
> guide words.
> EXAMPLE: **million / modern:** The word <u>minute</u> will appear
> on the page. The word <u>music</u> will not.

A. Circle each word that would be on a page with these guide words.

1. alive / arrest	2. flame / fourth	3. settle / sink
anxious	fourth	side
amount	flower	shawl
accept	fog	seed
arrest	figure	seventeen
actor	fly	sink
alive	flame	service
also	fox	settle
adventure	flew	sign
ant	from	sleep
ashes	flight	shelter
allow	fruit	space

B. Rewrite each group of words in alphabetical order. Then write the words that would be the guide words for each group.

1. _____ / _____

lawn _____

last _____

lamp _____

late _____

lap _____

lake _____

lead _____

2. _____ / _____

palm _____

page _____

pass _____

pad _____

pack _____

pan _____

pat _____

Using an Encyclopedia

- An **encyclopedia** is a reference book that has articles on many different subjects. The articles are arranged in alphabetical order in different books, called **volumes.** Each volume is marked to show which subjects are inside.
- **Guide words** are used to show the first subject on each page.
- There is a listing of **cross-references** at the end of most articles to related subjects that the reader can use to get more information on that subject.

A. Read the sample encyclopedia entry below. Use it to answer the questions that follow.

> **VITAMINS** are an important part of health. They cannot be produced by the body. Vitamins must be included in the diet. It is important to eat a variety of foods so your body will get all the vitamins it needs to stay healthy. Vitamins may be needed in increased amounts during periods of rapid growth, during stress, and while recovering from an illness. *See also* MINERALS.

1. What is the article about? _____

2. Why are vitamins important? _____

3. Why should you eat a variety of foods? _____

4. When might more vitamins be needed? _____

5. What other subject could you look at to get more information? _____

> **MINERALS** are elements that serve as building blocks or take part in chemical processes in the body. Most of the mineral content of the body is in the bones. Calcium is an important mineral that aids in the formation of teeth and bones, blood clotting, and the activity of muscles and nerves. Minerals are found in foods.

6. Why do you think this cross-reference is included in the article about vitamins? _____

_____

7. Does the above cross-reference mention vitamins? _____

> ■ When looking for an article in the encyclopedia:
> Always look up the last name of a person.
> EXAMPLE: To find an article on Babe Ruth, look under <u>Ruth</u>.
> Look up the first word in the name of a city, state, or country.
> EXAMPLE: To find an article on New York City, look under <u>New</u>. Look up the most important word in the name of a general topic.
> EXAMPLE: To find an article on the brown bear, look under <u>bear</u>.

B. Write the word you would look under to find an article on each of the following subjects.

1. Nelson Mandela _____

2. frozen food _____

3. United States _____

4. oceans of the world _____

5. Margaret Thatcher _____

6. United Kingdom _____

7. children's games _____

8. breeds of dogs _____

C. The example below shows how the volumes of one encyclopedia are marked. The subjects are in alphabetical order. Write the number of the volume in which you would find each article.

A	B	C-CH	CI-CZ	D	E	F	G	H	I-J	K	L
1	2	3	4	5	6	7	8	9	10	11	12
M	N	O	P	Q-R	S	T	U-V	W-X-Y-Z	INDEX		
13	14	15	16	17	18	19	20	21	22		

_____ 1. caring for horses

_____ 2. life stages of the butterfly

_____ 3. making paper

_____ 4. underwater plants

_____ 5. mammals

_____ 6. Buckingham Palace

_____ 7. yeast

_____ 8. redwood trees

Unit 6 Test

Choose the correct answer to each question.

1. Which word would be on a page with the guide words **able / again**?

   A ○ a   C ○ alone

   B ○ ago   D ○ afford

2. Which word would be on a page with the guide words **cold / contest**?

   A ○ come   C ○ code

   B ○ coin   D ○ corn

3. Which group of words is in correct alphabetical order?

   A ○ cub   B ○ debt

        cure   deck

        cry   deep

        cup   den

   C ○ girl   D ○ is

        glad   iron

        giggle   it

        glue   isn't

4. Which group of words is in correct alphabetical order?

   A ○ behold   B ○ chose

        believe   chat

        begin   cave

        bee   chef

   C ○ dot   D ○ apple

        doze   bear

        every   big

        fog   bang

5. Which word would be on a page with the guide words **dear / delight**?

   A ○ day   C ○ deck

   B ○ direct   D ○ demand

6. Which word would be on a page with the guide words **foam / foot**?

   A ○ found   C ○ foal

   B ○ for   D ○ fog

Use the sample encyclopedia article to answer the questions.

> **COAL** is a natural, black carbon solid used as fuel. For years it was our prime source of power. It is found underground and is made from layers of dead plants. *See also* FUEL.

7. What is the article about?

   A ○ fuel   C ○ dead plants

   B ○ coal   D ○ carbon

8. What is the cross-reference?

   A ○ fuel   C ○ underground

   B ○ carbon   D ○ layers

9. Where is coal found?

   A ○ fuel   C ○ underground

   B ○ carbon   D ○ layers

10. What is coal made from?

   A ○ dead plants   C ○ power

   B ○ fuel   D ○ underground

Use the sample encyclopedia article to answer the questions.

> **ELBOW** The elbow is a joint between the upper and lower arm. This joint allows the arm to bend, twist, and turn. Groups of muscles and tendons make the elbow work. One of the best tools the body has is the arm. It allows a person to reach out, hold, and control things. *See also* ARM *and* WRIST.

11. What is the article about?

    A ○ arms

    B ○ muscles

    C ○ elbows

    D ○ tendons

12. What are the cross-references?

    A ○ upper and lower arm

    B ○ muscles and tendons

    C ○ body and person

    D ○ arm and wrist

Choose the correct answer to each question about encyclopedias.

13. To find an article on the life of NASA astronaut John Glenn, which word would you look under?

    A ○ Glenn   **C** ○ John

    B ○ astronaut   **D** ○ NASA

14. Which volume would have an article about the mythical character Paul Bunyan?

    A ○ M   **C** ○ C

    B ○ P   **D** ○ B

15. To find an article about the different uses for diamonds, which word would you look under?

    A ○ gems   **C** ○ mining

    B ○ diamonds   **D** ○ uses

16. Which volume would have an article about the flight of whooping cranes in America?

    A ○ C   **C** ○ W

    B ○ A   **D** ○ F

Choose the volume in an encyclopedia where each article would be found.

A–C	D–F	G–I	J–L	M–N	O–Q	R–S	T–V	W–Z
1	2	3	4	5	6	7	8	9

17. Rosa Parks

    A ○ 1   **C** ○ 4

    B ○ 3   **D** ○ 6

18. the history of computers

    A ○ 1   **C** ○ 5

    B ○ 3   **D** ○ 7

19. the Amazon River

    A ○ 1   **C** ○ 8

    B ○ 7   **D** ○ 9

20. bald eagles

    A ○ 1   **C** ○ 6

    B ○ 2   **D** ○ 8

Answer Key

Assessment Test (P. 8)

A. 1. A **2.** H **3.** S **4.** S
B. 1. sound made with fingers
C. 1. S **2.** P **3.** C **4.** P
D. 1. won't **2.** I'm
E. 1. E, That is a great shirt! **2.** IN, Can't you see that it's too big? **3.** D, I think it fits just fine. **4.** IM, (You) Take it back to the store.
F. 1. It / <u>is raining</u> outside.
   2. <u>There</u> / <u>are</u> puddles in the street.
G. Sentences may vary. Suggested: Jerry went out to dinner at the new restaurant.
H. Alex cooked a big meal. He served it to his friends.

Assessment Test (P. 9)

I. The words in bold should be circled.
   Betty chose two <u>dogs</u>, **Yip** and **Yap**, to take home to her <u>children</u>.
J. <u>mailbox's</u>
K. 1. A **2.** L **3.** H
L. 1. future **2.** past **3.** present
M. 1. is **2.** come
N. 1. we **2.** them
O. The words in bold should be circled.
   We **carefully** planned an <u>exciting</u> <u>suprise</u> party for Henry.
P. 1. ever **2.** Those, don't

Assessment Test (P. 10)

Q.
                977 N. Seaside Dr.
                Ann Arbor, MI 68445
                Jan. 25, 19___

Dear Kathleen,
   Mario and I took Ginger to the vet to get her shots. She really hates to go!
   How is Frisky? I hope you are both fine.
                Your friend,
                Elena
R. The words in bold should be circled.
   We just moved into a new house.
   First, the dog next door began barking all night.
   Then we spoke to the neighbors. **Finally**, we had peace and quiet.
S. Statement: Taking a phone message
   I. Information needed from caller
      A. Name and number
      B. Message

Assessment Test (P. 11)

T. rich / rock
   1. rich **2.** right **3.** rinse **4.** rob **5.** rock
   baby / bat
   1. baby **2.** back **3.** ball **4.** base **5.** bat
U. 1. John James Audubon
   2. Audubon Society

V. 1. sea, 7 **2.** Hong, 3 **3.** nursing, 5 **4.** fly, 2 **5.** Keller, 4 **6.** aluminum, 1 **7.** vampires, 8 **8.** horses, 3 **9.** Shakespeare, 7 **10.** boomerangs, 1 **11.** instruments, 3 **12.** New, 5

Unit 1: Vocabulary

Synonyms (P. 13)

A. 1. desire **2.** outdoors **3.** seeing **4.** write **5.** match **6.** ask **7.** ideas **8.** little **9.** enjoy **10.** grew **11.** arranged
B. 1. common **2.** uncommon, active **3.** brave, halt **4.** stay **5.** glad, large

Antonyms (P. 14)

A. 1. sharp **2.** soft **3.** wrong **4.** save **5.** forget **6.** messy **7.** begin **8.** new **9.** top
B. Answers will vary. Suggested antonyms: big, clean, good, cleaned, brighten, drying, wrong, same

Homonyms (P. 15)

A. 1. its **2.** it's **3.** it's **4.** it's **5.** its **6.** its **7.** it's **8.** its **9.** it's
B. 1. There **2.** They're **3.** they're **4.** their **5.** there **6.** Their **7.** they're **8.** their

More Homonyms (P. 16)

A. 1. two, to **2.** too, to **3.** to **4.** two
B. 1. write **2.** right **3.** right **4.** right
C. 1. hear **2.** here, hear **3.** here, hear **4.** here

Multiple Meanings (P. 17)

A. 1. pillow **2.** salty liquid from the eye **3.** strike over and over **4.** make the sound of a bell **5.** loud noise **6.** heavy winds with rain or snow **7.** guide
B. Sentences will vary.

Prefixes (P. 18)

A. 1. disappear **2.** unconcerned **3.** unaware **4.** discover **5.** unharmed **6.** dislike **7.** disagree
B. 1. misunderstood **2.** misuse **3.** recreate **4.** relive **5.** misjudged **6.** react

Suffixes (P. 19)

A. 1. successful **2.** tireless **3.** effortless **4.** careless **5.** meaningful **6.** endless **7.** worthless **8.** joyless
B. 1. without color **2.** without a bottom **3.** full of sorrow **4.** full of beauty **5.** without flavor

Compound Words (P. 20)

A. 1. week, end **2.** home, made **3.** water, melon **4.** sun, set
B. 1. tugboat **2.** waterfront **3.** loudspeaker **4.** watchman **5.** fireplace
C. Sentences will vary. Suggested compound words: newspaper, midnight, notebook, baseball

Contractions (P. 21)

A. 1. I'll 2. we've 3. You'll 4. she's 5. he's
B. 1. can not 2. did not 3. will not 4. is not 5. we will

Unit 1 Test, Pages 22–23

1. B 2. B 3. A 4. D 5. A 6. C 7. B 8. D 9. C 10. B
11. B 12. A 13. D 14. C 15. C 16. D 17. A 18. C
19. D 20. B 21. C 22. B 23. A 24. D 25. D 26. B
27. A 28. B 29. B 30. B 31. D 32. D 33. C

Unit 2: Sentences

Recognizing a Sentence (P. 24)

A. 1. S 2. S 4. S 5. S 8. S
B. 1. S 2. Sentences will vary. 3. S 4. Sentences will vary. 5. S

Declarative and Interrogative (P. 25)

A. 1. interrogative 2. declarative 3. declarative
4. interrogative 5. declarative 6. interrogative
7. declarative 8. interrogative 9. declarative
10. interrogative 11. interrogative 12. declarative
13. interrogative 14. declarative 15. interrogative
16. interrogative 17. declarative 18. declarative
B. Sentences will vary.

Changing Sentences (P. 26)

A. 1. Am I finished? 2. Shouldn't you be finished?
3. Is this taking too long? 4. Are you leaving?
5. Can you stay?
B. Sentences may vary. Suggested:
1. Does Joe start his new job today?
2. Does he begin at nine o'clock?
3. Will he leave home at eight o'clock?
4. Does Joe like to work on cars?
5. Is repairing cars very interesting?
6. Is Joe sure he will like this job?
7. Will Joe do a good job?

Imperative and Exclamatory (P. 27)

A. 1. imperative 2. imperative 3. exclamatory
4. imperative 5. exclamatory 6. exclamatory
7. imperative 8. imperative 9. exclamatory
10. exclamatory 11. imperative 12. imperative
B. Sentences will vary.

Subjects and Predicates (P. 28)

A. Subjects will vary.
B. Predicates will vary.
C. 1. subject 2. predicate 3. predicate 4. subject
5. predicate 6. subject 7. predicate
D. 1. Tennis was invented by Major Walter Wingfield.
2. The game was called tennis-on-the-lawn.
3. Mary Outerbridge brought the game to the United States.
4. Tennis is a popular game.
5. Steffi Graf is a famous tennis player.
6. You can play tennis, too.

Simple Subjects and Predicates (P. 29)

A. Students should circle the words in bold.
1. The **plans** for a new car are made years ahead of time.
2. Many important **decisions** go into the design of a car.
3. Each **part** of the car is studied.
4. A clay **model** is made to show what the car will look like.
B. Students should circle words in bold.
1. Seven kinds of bears **live** in the world.
2. Most bears **live** in areas north of the equator.
3. Bears **have** small eyes.
4. Bears **can live** as long as thirty years.
5. A bear **uses** its claws to dig for food.
6. Brown bears usually **eat** grasses, berries, and nuts.
7. Seals and other animals **are** food for a polar bear.
8. Most bears **sleep** all winter.
9. Pandas **are** not really bears at all.
C. Subject   Predicate
1. game   was played
2. teams   played
3. game   was

Simple and Compound Sentences (P. 30)

A. 1. compound 2. compound 3. simple 4. simple
5. compound 6. simple 7. simple 8. compound
9. compound 10. simple
B. Sentences will vary.

Combining Sentences (P. 31)

A. Sentences may vary. Suggested:
1. We have to write a history report.
2. My subject is the Civil War and Robert E. Lee.
3. We must use the encyclopedia and other books.
4. I should stop wasting time and start my report.
B. Sentences may vary. Suggested:
1. Juan bought a big brown horse.
2. The horse is kept in an old red barn.
3. Juan and Lynn ride the horse in a field.
C. Sentences will vary.

Avoiding Run-on Sentences (P. 32)

Answers may vary. Some possible sentences follow.
1. One morning we found a baby bird.
2. It had been knocked from its nest by high winds.
3. Its mother was nowhere to be seen.
4. It was too young to fly.
5. We took it inside to care for it.
6. We were excited about taking care of the bird.
7. We didn't know what to do about feeding it.
Answers may vary. Suggested:
1. The bird's little mouth flew open so often that we could not find enough insects to feed it.
2. Then we found that the little bird liked dog food.
3. It also liked little bits of cooked egg yolk.
4. We even made some worms out of hamburger meat.

Unit 2 Test, Pages 33–34

1. D 2. B 3. A 4. D 5. B 6. D 7. C 8. A 9. C
10. A 11. C 12. D 13. D 14. B 15. C 16. C 17. B
18. D 19. B 20. C 21. B 22. C

Unit 3: Grammar and Usage

Nouns (P. 35)
A. 1. Mrs. Smith has a big job ahead.
2. She needs to plan a picnic for her family.
3. Mrs. Smith must find a big park.
4. The family always enjoys the picnic.
5. It is a big event every year.
6. Mr. Smith is planning some games.
7. He will set up a net for volleyball.
8. Margie will make the hamburgers.
9. Mrs. Smith finally picked Riverview Park.
10. The park is on the Mississippi River.
B. 1. thing 2. person 3. person 4. place 5. person
6. thing 7. place 8. person 9. place 10. person
11. place 12. thing 13. person

Proper and Common Nouns (P. 36)
A. 1. cousin, holidays 2. country 3. cousin, visitor
4. stories 5. year
B. 1. Dr. Alvarado, New York 2. Parkside Hospital
3. September 4. Roosevelt University; Queens,
New York 5. United States
C. Answers will vary.

Singular and Plural Nouns (P. 37)
A. 1. S; porches 2. S; chairs 3. P; girl 4. S; wives
5. P; fly 6. S; skies 7. P; fox 8. P; half 9. S; pencils
10. S; alleys 11. P; leaf 12. S; pouches 13. P; inch
14. S; shelves
B. Students should circle the words in bold.
1. plural   **programs**
2. singular   **hour**
3. singular   **time**
4. singular   **family**
5. plural   **magazines**
6. singular   **show**

Singular Possessive Nouns (P. 38)
A. 1. my aunt's house 2. my cousin's dog
3. my friend's books 4. my brother's bicycle
5. the cook's apron
B. 1. Jerry's 2. officer's 3. thief's 4. automobile's
5. city's
C. 1. store's 2. Lisa's 3. clerk's 4. bag's 5. man's

Plural Possessive Nouns (P. 39)
A. 1. sisters' 2. uniforms' 3. parents' 4. members'
5. instruments'
B. 1. Farmers' 2. children's 3. ponds' 4. sheep's
5. cows' 6. barns'

Action Verbs (P. 40)
A. 1. jumped 2. leaped 3. snapped 4. spun 5. arched
6. pulled 7. danced 8. howled 9. licked 10. yawned
11. chewed 12. snarled 13. teased 14. pulled
15. snapped 16. shot 17. bounded 18. scrambled
B. Predicates will vary.

Linking Verbs (P. 41)
A. Linking verbs may vary. Suggested:
1. is 2. grow 3. smells 4. look 5. seem 6. taste
7. sound 8. become
B. 1. L 3. L 5. L 6. L

Helping Verbs (P. 42)
Students should circle the words in bold.
1. **had** wanted 2. **had** planned 3. **has** gone
4. **were** waiting 5. **was** raking 6. **were** looking
7. **couldn't** find 8. **were** forced 9. **was** given
10. **is** going 11. **has** gone 12. **had** told
13. **was** going 14. **had** planned 15. **am** going
16. **have** seen 17. **are** taking 18. **is** meeting
19. **is** riding 20. **are** looking

Verb Tenses (P. 43)
A. 1. past 2. past 3. present 4. future 5. present
6. past 7. future 8. present 9. future 10. future
11. future
B. Verbs will vary.

Regular Verbs (P. 44)
A. 1. looked 2. gasped 3. settled 4. stepped 5. hurried
6. crushed 7. scratched 8. headed 9. changed
10. dropped
B. 1. sailed the boat 2. steered a straight course
3. carried the sail 4. enjoyed the fresh air and
sunshine

Irregular Verbs (P. 45)
1. went 2. left 3. took 4. knew 5. grew 6. saw
7. gave 8. sat 9. came 10. flew 11. said 12. began
13. wrote 14. broke 15. threw 16. chose 17. fell
18. ran

Making Subjects and Verbs Agree (P. 46)
1. eat; plural 2. lives; singular 3. fly; plural 4. feeds;
singular 5. scratch; plural 6. cause; plural
7. destroys; singular 8. fight; plural 9. slows; singular
10. acts; singular 11. drop; plural 12. watches;
singular 13. spread; plural 14. kills; singular
15. lose; plural 16. needs; singular 17. help; plural

Subjects and Linking Verbs (P. 47)
A. Answers may vary. Suggested:
1. was 2. was 3. were 4. is 5. are 6. are 7. is
8. is
B. Answers may vary. Suggested:
1. There are 2. There were 3. There is 4. There are
5. There are 6. There is 7. There are 8. There is

Subject Pronouns (P. 48)
A. 1. She 2. It 3. They 4. You 5. We 6. I 7. He 8. I
B. 1. I 2. We 3. He 4. It 5. They 6. you 7. She 8. I
C. Sentences will vary.

Object Pronouns (P. 49)
A. 1. it 2. us 3. me 4. us 5. them 6. you 7. him
8. me
B. 1. me 2. him 3. it 4. us 5. them 6. them 7. her
8. them
C. Sentences will vary.

Using Pronouns (P. 50)
1. We 2. They 3. It 4. them 5. us 6. He 7. him
8. she 9. her 10. us

Possessive Pronouns (P. 51)

1. My 2. our 3. Its 4. My or Our 5. his 6. his
7. her 8. our 9. Your or My 10. your or my 11. their
12. his or our 13. her 14. her 15. Their, Her, or Its
16. our 17. its, his, or her 18. my or our 19. Its
20. your

Adjectives (P. 52)

A. 1. big, tiny 2. sharp, bright 3. scared, small
4. speeding, wet 5. tired, dark 6. damp, big
7. little, wide
B. Answers may vary. Suggested:
Line 1. Many, beautiful Line 2. sparkling Line 3.
dark; Wild Line 4. green; Gentle Line 5. fierce
Line 1. young or strong; wooden or shaky
Line 2. strong or soft; thick Line 3. best or young;
shaky or wooden Line 4. six, red; soft Line 5. bare

Adjectives That Compare (P. 53)

A. 1. smallest 2. smaller 3. cutest 4. funnier 5. whitest
6. longest 7. naughtiest 8. harder 9. later 10. busier
11. happiest 12. biggest
B. 1. lighter 2. darkest 3. straighter 4. wildest 5. longer
6. shortest 7. longer 8. warmer 9. colder 10. coldest

Adverbs (P. 54)

A. 1. widely, cheerfully 2. Yesterday, calmly
3. quickly, loudly 4. Later, quietly
B. 1. quietly, how 2. softly, how 3. Later; when
4. there, where
C. Answers may vary. Suggested:
1. quickly 2. there 3. Suddenly 4. brightly
5. anxiously 6. slowly 7. totally 8. hopelessly
9. quietly

Adverbs That Compare (P. 55)

A. 1. faster 2. later 3. latest 4. sooner 5. most carefully
6. harder
B. 1. later 2. most quietly or quietest 3. more loudly or
louder 4. more peacefully 5. nearest 6. more slowly
or slower 7. sooner 8. more carefully

Using Words Correctly (P. 56)

A. 1. well, good 2. well 3. good 4. well 5. well 6. good
7. well 8. good 9. good 10. well 11. good
B. 1. any 2. any 3. nothing 4. ever 5. any 6. anything
7. anybody

Using Other Words Correctly (P. 57)

A. 1. those 2. them 3. them, them 4. those 5. them,
those 6. them 7. those 8. those
B. 1. don't 2. doesn't 3. doesn't 4. doesn't 5. don't,
doesn't 6. doesn't 7. don't 8. don't

Unit 3 Test, Pages 58–59

1. C 2. D 3. C 4. A 5. D 6. D 7. B 8. A 9. B 10. A
11. A 12. D 13. A 14. C 15. B 16. D 17. C 18. B
19. C 20. D 21. B 22. A 23. C 24. C 25. D 26. C
27. A 28. C

Unit 4: Capitalization and Punctuation

Names of People and Pets (P. 60)

1. Uncle George got up early today.
2. He and Aunt Beth had a special job to do.
3. Uncle George and Aunt Beth were going to the
animal shelter.
4. They wanted to find a puppy for Susan and
Michael.
5. Uncle George and Aunt Beth thought a small dog
would be nice.
6. But Susan and Michael wanted a big dog.
7. Uncle George saw a cute kitten named Mittens.
8. In the very last cage, they saw Sasha.
9. Uncle George and Aunt Beth loved her at once.
10. When Sasha ran circles around Michael, he loved
her, too.

Names of Places and Things (P. 61)

A. 1. Our family will spend Memorial Day in Washington.
2. We hope to see the White House and the
Washington Monument.
3. We also want to see the Smithsonian Institution.
4. The Potomac River forms a border between
Washington and Virginia.
5. The Lincoln Memorial is amazing to see at night.
6. The Vietnam Memorial gets many visitors.
7. There are many amazing sights in Washington.
B. Answers will vary.

Capitalizing Titles (P. 62)

A. 1. Doctor William H. Black 2. Judge Rosa Allen
3. A Wrinkle in Time 4. Captain William Faircroft
5. The President of the United States 6. Doctor Laurie
C. Bell 7. Attack of the Monster Plants
8. Major Carol Gates 9. Owls in the Family
10. My Side of the Mountain
B. 1. Mr. Thomas's 2. Judge George King
3. Judge King; Judge Claire Booth; Life in the Courts
4. Ms. Dias; Life in the Courts; Judge Booth
5. A Judge's Story; Raymond Field

Capitalizing Abbreviations (P. 63)

A. 1. Tues. 2. Wed. 3. Thurs. 4. Fri. 5. Sat. 6. Sun.
7. Jan. 8. Nov. 9. Sept. 10. Aug. 11. Oct. 12. Dec.
B. 1. The conference is planned for Aug. 12.
2. It will be held in Wm. Taft Park.
3. George W. Bush will be there.
4. Our mayor, Ms. Foster, was pleased he could come.
5. Police Chief E. S. Rodriguez will introduce him.
6. Many people want to hear Mr. Bush speak.
7. They want to know how he likes life away from
Washington, D.C.

Parts of a Letter (P. 64)

7216 melvin street
houston, tx 77040
october 23, 19__

dear fred,

I am doing a report on farm life. Do you have any information you can send me? My report must be turned in three weeks from today. I can really use any help you can give me. Pictures and facts would be helpful. The names of some books I could find at the library would also help a lot.

your friend,
jesse

---

820 w. state st.
lockhart, al 36455
october 29, 19__

dear jesse,

I'll be glad to help with your report. Better yet, why don't you come and visit? Call and let me know if you are coming. The library here serves all of alabama. I know we could find all the information you need.

your friend,
fred

Sentences (P. 65)

A. Students should circle the letters in bold.
1. **i** am going to ride my bike to the store. 2. **w**here is my bike? 3. **i**t is always in the garage by the hose.
4. **c**ould it be on the back porch? 5. **i**'ll ask Joanne if she has seen it. 6. **s**he said it was in the garage this morning. 7. **o**h, no, someone has stolen my bike!
8. **w**hat should I do now? 9. **w**ho could have taken it?
B. 1. I'll call the police about my bike. 2. Hurry, hurry, answer the phone! 3. Hello, is this the police station? 4. Yes, what can we do for you? 5. You must help me catch a bike thief. 6. How do you know your bike wasn't borrowed?

Using Commas in Sentences (P. 66)

1. I called Juan, Janet, and Karen last Saturday.
2. Yes, they wanted to have a picnic. 3. Juan packed a lunch, and Karen brought a backpack. 4. Well, we were finally ready to go. 5. Yes, we found a perfect place by the beach. 6. We played volleyball, swam, and hiked.
7. It was a great picnic, and there were no ants around.
8. We collected shells, driftwood, and pebbles. 9. Juan cleaned up the garbage, and Karen packed the leftovers.
10. We sang, laughed, and read.

Using Commas in Other Sentences (P. 67)

A. 1. Our neighbor, Buddy Rush, is gone.
2. Mr. Rush, his father, said he doesn't know where Buddy is. 3. Danny, did Buddy talk about going somewhere? 4. This seems very strange to me, Tim.
5. Chief Carter, our sheriff, thinks so, too. 6. Buddy, where are you? 7. Danny, don't you remember what I told you? 8. What should we do now, Chief Carter?
B. Students should put an X in front of these sentences.
1. Someone is talking to Craig. 2. Someone is talking to Lydia. 3. Mrs. Hicks is our neighbor. 4. Someone is talking to Carrie. 5. Anna is my dog.

Using Commas in Letters (P. 68)

A.

422 W. South St.
Dallas, TX 72843
November 12, 19__

Dear Mark,

Thank you for coming to my party. It was fun having you there. I also want to thank you for the great sweatshirt. It fits fine, and I really like it.

Your friend,
Theresa

8200 Columbus Ave.
Dallas, TX 72844
November 16, 19__

Dear Theresa,

Don't forget about the trip to the museum on Saturday. See you there.

Sincerely,
Mark

B. 1. 321 Pebble Beach Drive
Jacksonville, FL 32211
November 17, 19__
2. 101 Main St.
Oakland, CA 10032
July 10, 19__
C. 1. Dear Juana, 2. Sincerely yours, 3. Your friend,
4. Dear Grandmother, 5. Your grandson, 6. Hi, Scott,

Using Quotation Marks (P. 69)

1. "Do you want to talk about the interesting places we each visited this summer?" asked Ms. Chen. 2. "My sister and I visited my aunt in Nome, Alaska," said James. Or: James said, "My sister…Alaska." 3. "We flew to Quebec to see our grandmother," said Jenny. Or: Jenny said, "We flew…grandmother." 4. "We went to Arizona and saw the Grand Canyon," said Richard. Or: Richard said, "We went…Grand Canyon."

More About Quotation Marks (P. 70)

1. "Well," said Mike, "Dot is just getting over a strange accident." 2. "What happened?" asked Susan. 3. "A thought struck her," said Mike. 4. Jake asked, "Why did you throw the alarm clock out the window?"
5. "Because," said Joan, "I wanted to see time fly."
6. "What did one wall say to another?" asked Bonnie.
7. "I'll meet you at the corner," answered David.
8. "What gets wetter," Carlos asked, "the more you dry?"
9. "A towel does," said Angie. 10. Mother said, "Are your feet dirty?" 11. "Yes," replied Bobby, "but don't worry because I have my shoes on." 12. Maria asked, "How can you tell when an ice cube is nervous?"
13. "It breaks out," said Bill, "in a cold sweat."
14. Anna asked, "What is black-and-white and red all over?"
15. "It's a blushing zebra," said Jake. 16. "What did the rug say to the floor?" asked Mike. 17. "Don't move," replied Bonnie, "because I've got you covered."
18. Joan asked, "Why do sponges do a good job?"
19. "They become absorbed in their work," said Carlos.
20. Angie asked, "Why is a pencil like a riddle?"
21. "Because," said Maria, "it's no good without a point."